Special Thanks to:

Maxi Harper Graphics
Mike (R, S etc.)
Gail R

Well, hell, a bunch of people who don't necessarily want to see their names here.

Publisher Cataloging in Publication
Lapin, Lee
       The covert catalog2000/Lee Lapin – San Mateo, CA:
Intelligence Incorporated, c1999.
       p.cm
       Includes bibliographical references and contents
       ISBN 1-880231-19-0

363.2'89

1. Spying – Equipment and supplies. 2. Espionage – Equipment and supplies– Handbooks, manuals, etc. 3. Surveillance – Equipment and supplies, etc. I. Title.

**The Covert Catalog2000**

Additional copies of this book available from:

Intelligence Incorporated
3555 S. El Camino Real
San Mateo, CA 94403
www.intelligence.to

ISBN 1-880231-19-0

# IMPORTANT NOTICE

It IS illegal to possess devices which can be used to surreptitiously record conversations. It is illegal in many states to record *any* conversation, regardless of whether you are a part of it or not.

Video tape laws are constantly changing – laws dealing with a person's expectation to privacy are in effect and also subject to change.

This book is NOT a solicitation to sell or purchase any equipment or services. If you are considering any purchase you must consult with an attorney who knows the status of the latest laws and regulations.

This is not just a disclaimer – within the previous few years the US government has arrested numerous people for sales and possession of illegal spying devices.

Intelligence Incorporated, Lee Lapin and any and all dealers accept no responsibility for illegal use of any materials contained within this book.

The **Covert Catalog2000** is designed to provide direct access to manufacturers, distributors and certain dealers of electronic surveillance equipment, counter measures gear, covert and security video cameras, transmitters and systems, specialized covert entry devices, unusual weapons, training providers, specialized newsletters and magazines as well as other items of interest for those in the surveillance, security and investigative fields.

The majority of these suppliers will deal with anyone on a direct basis, although a few are wholesale only, and fewer still, law enforcement only.

The Covert Catalog2000 encompasses several years of research and is, I believe, the most complete such guide ever assembled. Many of these sources do not appear in any other collection.

A few things to note:

•	I have purposely not included most of the "spy shops" one can find by simply going on the internet and entering an appropriate key word such as "spy". Reason? Almost all such come-and-go operations are simply reselling the same equipment included herein.

Generally for a much higher price.

•	Many, if not most of the equipment manufacturers which aim for wholesale markets will sell a "sample" to interested parties who might become larger customers down the line. Many will also sell overruns – all will refer a potential customer to a dealer if necessary.

•	Every source has been verified as we go to press. Most contact information should remain valid for years  – on the other hand, web sites come and go, search the net by utilizing any of the popular search engines for the latest URL's.

•	Please check our web site for updates and ancillary materials – www.intelligence.to. No net., no com., just remember "to intelligence".

Enjoy.

lee

# NOTES

I have employed several acronyms in this publication the reader should be aware of:

- OEM Original Equipment Manufacturer
- OPS Other People's Stuff
- LE Law Enforcement

Always check with the supplier for the latest price and ordering instructions before placing an order. If I have designated the source as primarily wholesale oriented, it would advantageous to place any "sample" orders on a dealer's letterhead.

Most of the sources will furnish a catalog or PR materials upon request. If there is a charge for catalog materials it usually falls between $3.00 – $5.00, one might be wise to include this fee with the original request, or at least offer to cover any expenses.

Many companies are switching to internet sites rather than printed catalogs, try a web search before attempting a written communication.

Finally, I've tried to construct this book as to be an enjoyable read whether the reader is looking to actively make a purchase or simply to view the state of the art in neat stuff...

# The Covert Catalog2000

### by lee lapin

# CONTENTS

# ELECTRONIC SURVEILLANCE

# AUTO TELECODER
## Model
# TR-505

Apart from the similar models heretofore in use, this model can be used safely in any areas, and it can be applied to any taperecorders and radio-cassette recorders.

Kant Corporation Seku Bldg., 3-4-5 Nishi Shinbashi Minato-Ku, Tokyo, 105 Japan. Kant is a time proven supplier of some nice taps and bugs for VLP (Very Low Prices, or perhaps Very Lonely People). The real cheapies are VHF but they also offer a couple of crystal controlled room and phone units as well as pen transmitters, calculator bugs, thru wall and recorder starters.

You know they've got to be okay because of the descriptive language ("do not touch the microphone and the lead wire so that fricative or creaky noises may be heard") and hand drawn equipment graphics.

continued on next page

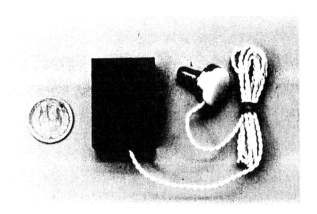

You can listen to a conversation beyond a thick concrete wall or in the next room clearly.

A combination of the most modern electronic technology and acoustic oscillatory engineering has given birth to this epoch-making "Wall Microphone". Unlike other acoustic amplifier, it turns oscillations transferred to the wall into voice waves. It certainly deserves to be called a "real wall microphone for professional use."

**Thrifty Spy Mart** POB 2327 Acworth, GA 30102. Another spy shop gone mail order. Resellers of Capri countermeasures, various covert cameras, lockpicks, Dan Gibson, Silver Creek, some Japanese pinhole cameras.

**USI Corporation POB 2052, Melbourne, FL 32901.** At one time USI offered some of the best ES equipment/deals around. This is because they were reselling Winston Arrington's (Sheffield Electronics) transmitters.

After an alleged talk between some nice Feds and Mr. A, these units are no longer offered *anywhere*. USI still resells some covert video stuff, recorders, recorder phone starters and a 3 channel, crystal controlled transmitter/receiver/recorder package (looks like a body wire) at a fairly reasonable price.

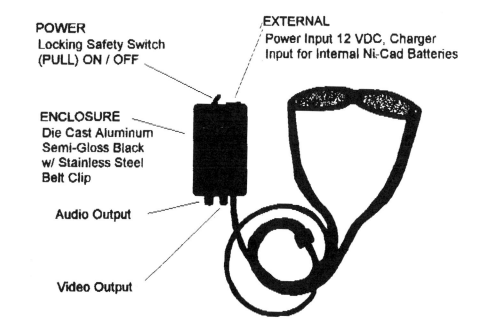

**POWER**
Locking Safety Switch (PULL) ON / OFF

**EXTERNAL**
Power Input 12 VDC, Charger Input for Internal Ni-Cad Batteries

**ENCLOSURE**
Die Cast Aluminum Semi-Gloss Black w/ Stainless Steel Belt Clip

Audio Output

Video Output

**TRANSMITTER**
Size - 2"x 3"
2000' range (line of sight)
170 MHZ - range
Sens.: 85 db  spl@ ±7khz FM
8 Channels available
Freq. Response: 100-10,000 hz
Battery life: 9V Alkaline=12 hrs.
         9V Lithium=20 hrs.

**Singa Takara Enterprise, Inc.** No. 238 Chilin Road, Taipei, Taiwan ROC www.commerce.com./tw /e. STE is probably the largest and very definitely one of the best, manufacturers of "civilian" (although they sell to many police and intelligence sources) the world has to offer.

After the "spy shop" busts both Cony and Micro and Security moved, stopped talking to Americans and refuse to ship to the US. This company is the recommended replacement.

See the *very same products* sold at several times the price in various US and English surveillance catalogs...

Prices start (for single units) at $23.00 US and climb way up to a whopping $275.00 for the top of the heap transmitters.

### TKS-103

1. Measurment : 27x22x22mm
2. Transmitting distance : 300 meters
3. 3 channels (A.B.C)
4. Set it to molular jack by one touch
5. No battery required

### TKS-001
1. Transmiter Frequency : 75-88 MHz ( adjustable)
2. Transmitter distance : 30-50 meters
3. No battery required
4. Just set the clip to the telephone line
5. Measurment : 30x21x12mm

### TKS-105
**UHF CARD TYPE TRANSMITTER**
1. Measuremert : 85x53x4.5mm
2. Battery : CR2430x1pce.
3. 3Channels(A,B &C).
4. VOX(Voice Acitivated mode) or Normal selectable.

### TKS-2
**SPERCIAL WALL MICROPHONE**
1. Improved unit of MW-33
2. High sensitivity
3. Measuremert : 20x70x54mm
4. Battery : 6F22 or 6LR61(9V)x1pce

### TKS-2
**SPERCIAL WALL MICROPHONE AND UHF RECEIVER**
1. High sensitivity ceramic microphone
2. Transmit cleen sound by UHF wave
3. Measuremert : 15x38x61mm
4. Battery : LR1(1.5v)x2pcs or R1 (1.5v)x2pcs
5. Receivers : TKS-1053 UHF mini receiver

## Advanced Security System from a Superior Manufacturer

SUN-MECHATRONICS specializes in highly advanced security products. We offer various wireless transmitting/receiving systems for use in police and law enforcement agencies, wall contact microphones, foolproof bug detectors and high-performance pinhole lenses for video movie cameras. For more Details, see our homepage.

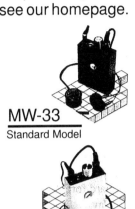

### MW-33
Standard Model

### BC-700
UHF Clip Type
TEL Transmitter

### UZ-220/110
UHF AC Tap
Type Transmitter

### UZ-110 CORD
UHF AC Tap
Type Transmitter

### UZ-220/110 BERO
UHF AC Tap Type Transmitter

### SK-300
High Sensitivity
Ceramic MIC Model

### BC-700
UHF Modular Connector
Type TEL Transmitter

### UCR-500EX
UHF 5 Hours Automatic
Receiving Recorder

### VP-37WXi
Right Image & Small Pinhole

### CD-Voxer
UHF Card Type
Transmitter

### UCR-120DX
UHF Automatic
Receiving Recorder

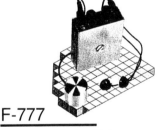

### F-777
4ch Selectable Amplifying
ModelStandard Model

### MT-600
UHF Modular Connector
Type TEL Transmitter

### VP-37EX
Right Image & Wide View

**ALL PRODUCTS COMPLETELY MADE IN JAPAN**

### FIBERVISION 6000
Fiber Scope

### BUG CHASER
2-Mode Newest
Bug Detector

### UCL-201
UHF Calculator
Type Transmitter

### UZ-100
UHF Pocketable
Receiver

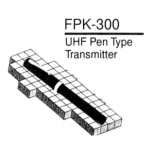

### FPK-300
UHF Pen Type
Transmitter

# NEW!

### ULX-40
UHF Extra Long Term
Built in MIC Transmitter
*260 Hours - Manganese AA (R6P)
Over 600 Hours - Alkaline AA (LR6)

### UPX-40
UHF High Power Built-in
MIC Trramsmitter
*150%-200% Wider Cover Area
Than UZ-400

9V (6F22 or
6LR61) x1

AA (R6 or
LR6) x2

Sun-Mechatronics Co., LTD. 3-37 Kandasakumacho, Chiyoda-ky, Tokyo, Japan www.sun-mechatronics.co.ip. Another terrific Asian Supplier of good, but K-Mart priced surveillance gear.

**Lorraine Electronic Surveillance** 716 Lea Bridge Road, London E10 6AW UK. Established in 1975 Lorraine is a leader in the sales of moderate to fairly sophisticated ES and TSCM equipment.

A number of their units including scrambled series and parallel phone taps (which require a matching receiver to demodulate) are quite unique. Having the transmission scrambled effectively limits accidental listeners, and to some extent, discovery by those searching for electronic invaders.

**HOWEVER** simple frequency inversion can be easily defeated by anyone willing to invest a few bucks (see Ramsey Electronics, Information Unlimited) and who recognizes the distinctive "Donald Duck" sound of this form of scrambling.

Don't think the transmission is secure from any professional.

They sell room bugs (scrambled and otherwise) in wall outlets, calculators, extension plugs, etc. Telephone taps can be purchased inside of common RS-232 wall boxes.

In addition to what appears to be their own OEM equipment Lorraine also resells a number of more common Japanese entries such as the thru wall amplifier, card transmitter, pen transmitters, long play recorders, interfaces, telephone starters.

Neat stuff, great catalog BUT the Japanese entries can be purchased directly from several Asian dealers at a great savings.

Lorraine is medium to high priced.

**▲ UXT TELEPHONE TRANSMITTER**

Both sides of a conversation are automatically transmitted when a telephone handset is lifted. Connected in series, the UXT can be installed inside a specific instrument or along the telephone wiring. Normally used on direct telephone lines, this product can also work with instruments connected to some electronic micro processor controlled systems.'

**▼ UX-DS POWER SOCKET TRANSMITTER**

Indistinguishable from an ordinary electrical socket, miniature electronics are concealed within a functioning U.K. standard double switched power outlet. The transmitter operates continually using the mains power supply. UX-DS offers more assured permanence as it is unlikely to be removed.

**▼ UX-DS (S) SCRAMBLED POWER SOCKET TRANSMITTER**

The scrambled UX-DS renders your surveillance operation unintelligible to an unauthorised listener. *PLEASE ENQUIRE ABOUT AVAILABILITY OF NON-U.K. SOCKETS.*

$119.00 With Free 50' Cable.
**New!** Same Size In Color
**$385.00**
Economy Color $249.00
**Free Over Night Shipping***

**Spy Company** 7954 Transit Rd., Suite 216 Williamsville, NY 14221 www.spycompany.com. Resellers, Sony, several drop out relays, long play recorders, Japanese covert and pinhole cameras, pen register, lockpicks, nothing too unique but prices aren't terrible, might be worth a price check before ordering elsewhere.

**The Counter Spy Shop Antwerpen** Postbus 500 B-2000 Antwerpen I. A veritable plethora of surveillance and counter surveillance gear from 30+ OEM's. OptoElectronics receivers, British probe microphones, Japanese and German taps and bugs, Canadian Parabolic mics, American recorders and "bug detectors"...

Highish prices, but one stop shopping includes Laser monitoring systems, impossible to find telephone drop-in transmitters, off-the-American market Cony bugs, PK Electronics tap-in-a-capacitor, Radio Shack telephone starters and Shomer-Tec hold invaders.

Even, what I think is a parabolic microphone hidden, KGB style, in an ordinary umbrella.

I say I think, because the damn catalog is in Dutch. However they are considerate enough to put the price and a short description in English on a separate sheet. Catalog is 60 Guilders (about $30).

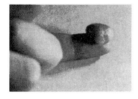

### Pijltjes- en werpzender

Vaak laten de omstandigheden het niet toe een ruimte te betreden en kan men slechts van buitenaf afluisteren. Ook in die gevallen moet een onopvallende audiobewaking gegarandeerd zijn. Voor deze situaties biedt de Counter Spy Shop de pijltjes- en werpzender. De zenderpijltjes kunnen door middel van een pistool tot op 25 m afstand in het beoogde doel worden geschoten. De pijltjes doordringen o.a. hout en poreuze muren. Wil men echter door een muur of een raam heen afluisteren dan biedt de werpzender uitkomst. Deze zender wordt als een balletje klei tegen het raam geworpen. De klei droogt na 1-2 dagen op waarna de zender op de grond valt.

### Combinatie telefoon- en ruimte zenders

Deze zenders kunnen zowel als ruimte- en als telefoon zender worden gebruikt en worden gevoed door de telefoonlijn zelf, waardoor ze een lange gebruiksduur geven. Zodra er een telefoongesprek wordt gevoerd worden de ruimte geluiden onderdrukt om het telefoongesprek zo duidelijk mogelijk uit te zenden. Als de telefoon op de haak ligt schakelt de zender automatisch over op ruimte zender. De Counter Spy Shop levert tevens een telefoon- en ruimte zender in capsule vorm (1323) voor een snelle en eenvoudige installatie.

### Riem zender

Kwartsgestuurde zender verborgen in de gesp van een lederen riem met ingebouwde antenne.

**Jiun An Technology Co., Ltd.**, 1F No. 12, Shao Hsing St., Taipei, Taiwan www.asiansources.com/jiunan.co. Another Japanese supplier of bugs, phone taps, receivers, and a rather unique infrared laser video camera that will tape at distances up to 100 meters in total darkness.

Reasonable, can be ordered on-line.

## JIUNAN-07 PBX System Transmitter & Receiver

**Key Specifications/Special Features:**

- **Included in the system:**
  - PT-01 Transmitter
  - PR-11 Receiver
- **PR-11 Receiver**
  1. 99-channel number
  2. Frequency Range: 138.00 ~ 174.00MHz
  3. Monitors conversation via on-panel speaker or earphone
  4. With external speaker jack, can be connected with VCVA recorder
  5. Power TX output: 1W/2.5W/5W
  6. Sensitivity: 138.00 ~ 174.00MHz, -12dB
  7. Sinad: -123dBm, -20dB Sinad: -120dBm
  8. Mil-810C & FCC Part 90 qualifications
  9. Power: DC 9V ~ 13.8V
  10. Dimensions: 110 x 60 x 40mm
  11. Weight: 420g (including battery)

## JIUNAN-02 Infrared Laser Video Camcorder

**Key Specifications/Special Features:**

- **IL-40 Infrared Laser System**
  1. Special designed for totally dark circumstances and long distance range
  2. Observation distance: at least 100m
  3. Compatible with any brand of B/W CCD camera, Sony TRV-Series 0 Lux Color Camcorder and night vision systems
  4. Lighting angle adjustable from 1~40°
  5. Invisible infrared laser
  6. Wave length: 830nm
  7. Output power: 40mW
  8. Power: DC 3V (use CR-123A, lasts for 4 hours)
  9. Lightweight: 100g
  10. Compact size: diameter 24 x 125mm

## SPRACHÜBERWACHUNG - AUDIO SURVEILLANCE

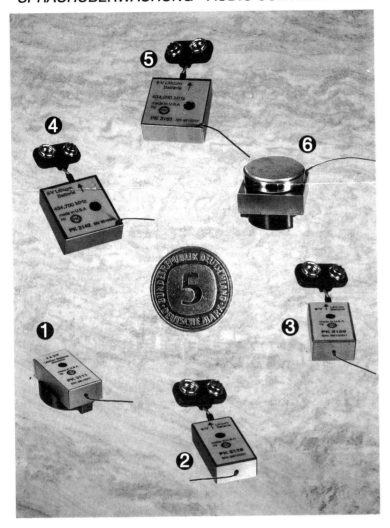

### Technische Spezifikation

**1. QUARZ-TELEFONSENDER**          Ord.Nr. 07226 BV

*Mit seinen extrem winzigen Abmessungen, bei gleichzeitig sehr hoher Ausgangsleistung, handelt es sich bei diesem Sender um den letzten Stand der technischen Entwicklung. SMD-Bestückung. Absolute Frequenzstabilität. Dieser Sender ist speziell für die Übertragung von Telefongesprächen konzipiert. Das Gerät arbeitet nur während Telefonaten. Leichte Installation an beliebiger Stelle der Telefonleitung, Verteilerkasten oder Telefondose. Unbegrenzte Betriebsdauer. Reichweite bis max. 300 mtr. möglich.*

**2. QUARZ-TELEFONSENDER, XL**          Ord.Nr. 07227 BV

*Profi-Ausführung mit extra hoher Ausgangsleistung. SMD-Bestückung. Absolute Frequenzstabilität. Dieser Sender ist speziell für die Übertragung von Telefongesprächen konzipiert. Das Gerät arbeitet nur während Telefonaten. Leichte Installation an beliebiger Stelle der Telefonleitung, Verteilerkasten oder Telefondose. Unbegrenzte Betriebsdauer. Reichweite bis max. 800 mtr. möglich.*

**3. TELEFON-TONBANDSTEUERUNG**          Ord.Nr. 08171

*Beim Abheben des Telefonhörers schaltet sich das angeschlossene Tonband bzw. Cassettenrekorder ein, zeichnet das Gespräch beider Teilnehmer auf und schaltet nach Auflegen des Hörers wieder ab. Wird zwischen Telefon und Tonband/Cassettengerät angeschlossen. Einfache Installation. Kann an beliebiger Stelle der Telefonzuleitung (z.B. im Keller) erfolgen. Durch Telefonstrom-Speisung unbegrenzte Betriebsdauer. Handelsübliche Bandgeräte anschliessbar.*

Ord.Nr. 45081

**1. RAUMSENDER, Quarzstabil**          Ord.Nr. 03111 BV

*Dieser quarzstabilisierte Raumsender bietet hohe Ausgangsleistung bei gleichzeitig sehr geringen Abmessungen. Der Sender ist mit einem Spezialmikrofon bestückt, welches sich auf die jeweils vorhandenen Lautstärkebedingungen automatisch einstellt, dadurch ist es möglich auch Gespräche aus größerer Distanz zufriedenstellend und ohne Lautstärkeminderung zu übertragen. Reichweite bis 300 m möglich.*

## Notes From The Underground

As anyone who has been reading the papers during the last couple of years is aware of – the Spy Factory chain was closed down and its owner (a former DEA agent) arrested for selling devices "primarily designed for the surreptitious interception of conversation.

The units in question were mainly from Micro and Security Electronics in Japan. These small efficient transmitters have been the backbone of audio surveillance for years.

The Customs department along with the NYPD went so far as to set up a US company where anyone could purchase the units at a small markup over the original Japanese price.

This firm encouraged sales to other dealers.

Customs monitored the sales for some time and finally arrested a bunch of dealers, one fairly inside source indicates the arrests were based on which blatant lawbreakers had the most money for fines...

**TOP Electronics** Wilhelm-Paul-Str., 12, D-63456 Hanau, Germany. A very interesting reseller of a mish mash of surveillance/counter gear. Sources I can recognize include Opto, AOR, several Asian video manufacturers, English wireless mics, etc.

But, *but*, besides the selection of covert video cameras, parabolic and directional mics, long play and digital recorders, one can select from a number of telephone taps and room bugs, origin unknown (probably from another German designer who does not usually market in the US).

Some interesting options, prices not too bad; yes the catalog is in German...

**Confidential Communications LTD.**, 344 Kilburn Ln., London, England W9 3 EF. Neat catalog, neat stuff. Some very definitely imported from one or more of our Asian friends and marked up a trifle, some I'm not exactly sure where it/they originate.

Besides the usual bugs-in-lamps-outlets-calculators combined with taps-in-jacks they have a few really unique products. A pen register (dialed number recorder) that transmits the data to a surveillance receiver, combined receiver/recorders, non-law enforcement slave units, some countermeasure goods and encryption devices.

Prices in the mid – to reasonable arena.

# Multi-Line Monitoring

## TL-25

This unit has a line-select facility to allow managers to select the line of their choice and record or listen at a distance when risk control so requires. Connect the TL-25 to 5 lines and from a simple thumb wheel switch you can select the target line for recording, moreover the small pocket sized receiver will **monitor all incoming and outgoing calls** to allow you to listen instantly to what's going on.

This equipment is ideal for sales training, sales monitoring, **Management Risk Control** and anywhere random monitoring is required.

The **UX102D** is a disguised Telephone Transmitter using the same digital technology as the UX102 but cleverly secreted inside a telephone plug or socket splitter.

## UX102D

**Confidential Order Line**
+44 (0) 181 968 0227

# Cordless Data Interceptor

The **UX500** is designed to receive data from target telephone lines where small digital transmitters are fitted within the line.

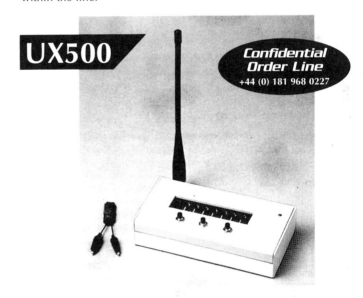

## UX500

**Confidential Order Line**
+44 (0) 181 968 0227

All the Alpha numeric data which the caller inputs with his keypad on the phone will transmit to the high quality receiver and over 100 alpha numeric data entries will record in the memory. The UX-500 can be connected to the RS-232 Serial port of your PC and all data will log into your computer.

The UX-500 is the ideal device for companies for whom transactions and authorisations are issued by automatic telephone answering services and where they would like to keep this data for their records.

- *Receives and records DTMF data on the telephone or fax line.*
- *Capable of receiving data via RS232 interface.*
- *Completely wireless connection - requires no hard wire installation.*
- *Features UHF transmitter/receiver.*

**Reinaert Electronics** POB 93014 1090 BA Amsterdam, The Netherlands. RE has spent the last 30 years dealing with the design and manufacture of electronic materials. They have traditionally specialized in night vision design for both civilian and military use. They also repair foreign brands and do custom design.

In addition they have "over 30,000 types of electronic components and products in stock including IR cameras, covert video gear (including a new transmitter), monitoring systems, countermeasures gear and so on.

RE is significant for one other major product – a laser audio surveillance system. Their unit appears very similar in design to the system formerly produced by PK Electronics in Germany.

The laser and the receiver are both housed in a camera body (ideal for camouflage as well as providing a ready mount for the necessary optics). The invisible IR laser is focused on a window where it is modulated by audio on the other side of the window pane, reflected back, picked up by the receiver and demodulated.

RE claims a range of 3000' is possible and they sell the unit for $25,000. RE does not have a full catalog but would be happy to provide a quote on any equipment you are planning to purchase, although as their manager told me, "we are selling so many of the laser units most of our time is spent keeping up with that demand."

**Shomer-Tec** Box 28070 Bellingham, WA 98228. One of the better general catalogs on the market – one can purchase top quality law enforcement, military and survival gear including waterproof gear bags, knives, handcuffs, clothing, light sticks, all in all a very complete grouping.

However our interest focuses on a line of gear designed by Shomer-Tec's own electronics engineer. This particular line is useful, unique, very reasonably priced and not to be found elsewhere (except when other dealers buy from ST and boost the prices).

# TELE-MONITOR 2000

The Tele-Monitor 2000 is a very sophisticated audio monitoring device. Utilizing advanced logic-chip technology, it enables you to discreetly listen in on your premises via regular telephone lines  from any telephone in the world! The Tele-Monitor 2000 requires no activating beeper or whistle, does not

affect normal incoming and outgoing calls, and offers unprecedented capability and flexibility by allowing up to 4 units per line to be connected. It allows you to listen in on your premises with ease! The unit's sensitive microphone will pick up even a whisper up to 35 feet away. The Tele-Monitor 2000 requires a two-step user identity verification process before allowing monitoring access. This latest model also has a "quick access" mode option for applications on a dedicated line. To monitor, just dial your phone number from any tone telephone, access the monitor, and then push the button on the phone corresponding to the area you wish to listen in on. You may "move" around the premises (if you have multiple units connected) as much as you desire — just push the number of the desired area and it instantly transfers monitoring to that zone. You can switch between areas as much as you like for as long as you like. Or, by pushing "5", you can monitor all areas simultaneously. The Tele-Monitor 2000 is a completely self-contained unit; no actual telephone is required for its operation.

Equipped with modular plugs for instant connection to telephone jacks. Needs no batteries. Size: $3^1/_2$" x $5^1/_2$" x 1".

TM-2000 ....................................................... Tele-Monitor 2000 ....................................................

# THE INFORMER

The Informer is an amazing telephone line device that allows you to listen in to a room <u>after</u> the called party has hung up! You can "plant" a

desired topic near the end of a conversation, and you'll likely hear them discuss their *real* thoughts on the subject as soon as they hang up. When you call to the home or business where the Informer has been installed, after the conversation is completed (or even just a "sorry, wrong number" ), let them hang up first. You will then have the option of being able to clearly monitor all the audio activity in the room in which The Informer is located, even though they've already hung up their phone! We originally designed this unit for a leading law enforcement agency as a special device that they could supply to certain citizens who were at particular risk of being held hostage in their own home or office. In such a case, agents would have the ability to remotely, discreetly, and safely monitor the area to verify status and collect real-time intelligence. The Informer plugs into a standard modular telephone jack. Size: $3^1/_2$" x $5^1/_2$" x 1". WARNING: this device is to be used only in a legal and lawful manner in compliance with all applicable laws and F.C.C. regulations.

TIP ................................................................ The Informer ....................................................

# THE "X" PHONE

THE "X" PHONE works and looks like a standard telephone. But is also has the capability to function as an advanced remote audio monitoring device. It's so sophisticated that you don't even need to call in to see if there's activity in the area; it will continuously monitor the area and call <u>you</u> when something is happening. When audio activity occurs in the area of THE "X" PHONE, it silently and automatically calls the telephone number you have programmed. When you answer, you are immediately and clearly listening to all of the audio activity in the area of THE "X" PHONE. The intruders there have no idea whatsoever that the innocuous-looking telephone over there has not only detected them, but has already called you and you're listening to every word they're saying! You can then call 911 or take other appropriate action. It can be an effective component of your home or business security system. THE "X" PHONE can be programmed to call any telephone in the world, and the number to be called can be changed as often as you require. Additionally, this sophisticated unit has the capabilities to provide unprecedented and devastating new surveillance options; however, you are warned that it is to be used only in a legal and lawful manner in compliance with all applicable laws and FC. regulations. Simple to use— it operates as a fully functioning regular telephone until you activate it. When you leave your home or business, just punch in the telephone number of where you'll be at, flick the special switch on the phone, and you're set. It will call you when there's something you need to hear.

TXP ................................................................ THE "X" PHONE ....................................................

As any eavesdropper worth his or her salt will tell you the best way to get an audio signal, say a conversation, from place A to place B is to place a microphone at point A and run a wire to point B.

Hardwired microphones can be discovered by counter measure types, or just curious people by discovering and following the wires, by attaching a tone generator to any suspicious wires (which will make the mic "squeal") use of non-linear junction detectors and on occasion by the use of heterodyning sounds which beat against the mic element causing audio to be produced.

I just saw a demonstration of a unique new device which alleviates all the above problems. Invented by those same nice folks who designed the Israeli cell phone blocker discussed in an earlier issue, the SOM - 010/01 is a tiny, tiny plastic chamber with a movable diaphragm covering one end.

The unit contains no metal whatsoever, requires a 1 millimeter hole into the target area and is sensitive enough to pick up normal conversation at the rear of 20' x 40' room.

The unit is attached to a fiber optic cable slightly thicker than the human hair. It terminates in a palm sized transmitter/receiver. The system sends two beams of coherent light down the fiber optics where it is modulated by audio at the chamber end. The returning beam is "read" and the audio output to a speaker, recorder, etc.

Advantages to this system include:

•       Extreme sensitivity. It did work exactly as advertised and returned clear audio
•       Sub-miniature size
•       No metal parts
•       No wire
•       Fiber optic cable doesn't need to be cut to a certain length because of very little line loss (can be run 1 mile, down 3 dB, five miles with out major signal degeneration)
•       Fiber optics not subject to electrical interference, can be run along side or *inside* electrical wiring.
•       FO can be run through weather, even under water.

**phone-or** 13 Altalef St., POB 2756, Yehud, 56216, Isreal.

Option "A"

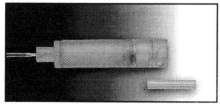

Option "A" with Extention Tube

**Information Unlimited** 344 Kilburn Lane, London W9 3EF, England. Not only do these guys have the same name as another interesting entry in the field of electronic surveillance, an astute reader might also note they have the same address as yet another supplier...

Latter explanation being that IU is a separate branch that imports pretty cool Japanese products exclusively and resells them to nice folks that don't have the Japanese connection.

A) **FX-101:** Through away Room Transmitter: Simply connect to a 9v battery and drop it in the target area. This transmitter will pick up even a whisper from ten metres away and transmit the voice to your air band receiver for listening or recording.

B) **TX-101:** Compact and Powerful Room Transmitter: It is only 20mm x 20mm x 5mm and it includes a watch battery which will last for 3 working days. This transmitter will transmit on FM band 75MHz-108MHz which you can receive with your own FM radio or Multi Band radio.

C) **FX-105:** Multi Plug Transmitter: Similar plug can be found in home and offices. Just change the existing plug with FX-105 and listen to the conversation on an air band radio. As it works with mains there is no need for battery and will last as long as it is required.

D) **FX-107:** Fully Functional Calculator which is armed with a room transmitter. It is activated with a hidden switch and the conversation can be received via an air band radio.

E) **FX-102:** The smallest Telephone Transmitter: The FX-102 is connected parallel to any where on the line or inside the telephone socket. The conversation can be picked up by air band radio.

F) **CX-01:** Crystal Controlled Room Transmitter with Receiver: It requires no adjustment or tuning. The transmitter & receiver are matched and as soon as it is switched on, you can hear crystal clear the room conversation taking place. Designed and manufactured in Japan.

G) **CLX-130:** Crystal Controlled Calculator Transmitter. The calculator is fully functional and will only transmit when switched on by a hidden switch. (Made in Japan.)

H) **CA-10:** Crystal Controlled Telephone Transmitter and Receiver: Designed for professional use at unattended operations. The transmitter requires no battery and the receiver can be connected to a voice activated recorder. We supply all the accessories you need for intelligence action.

**Surveillance Technology Group** 540 W. Boston Post Road, Mamaroneck, NY 10543. STG claims to have 30 years experience in the design and manufacture of "advanced covert audio surveillance systems used by government agencies and law enforcement groups worldwide".

Most units can be identified by an astute reader as Japanese or other foreign sources, a few may be OEM.

Probably LE only at this point in time.

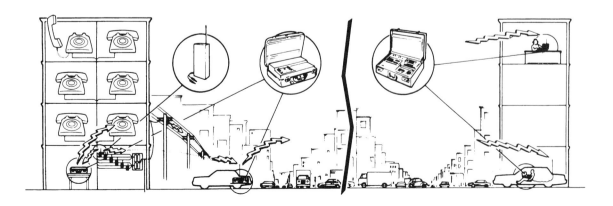

**Eskan Electronics LTD.,**
168 Caledonian Rd,
London N1 0SQ UK One
of the larger mid to upper
end suppliers of ES,
TSCM and video gear in
the world. Eskan goes
from the sublime to
overkill –

Starting with the latter
would be their Global
Listening System which is
capable of monitoring up
to 100 transmitters which
can be keyed on and off
remotely, tape recorders
which download at high
speed to the
eavesdropper and has
bells and whistles all over
the map.

They offer a line of
VHF/UHF room and
telephone transmitters,
(average price about
$400) many of which can
be adapted to other uses
(body worn, car, etc. with
an adapter or two.

# ENTRY LEVEL AUDIO SURVEILLANCE

If an operation is long-term or
access to the target area is
restricted then mains powered
transmitters are the solution.
They are maintenance free and

**KIT ONE    ROOM SURVEILLANCE SYSTEM**
Consists of an RT1 room transmitter and AR1 receiver in a
presentation case.

**KIT TWO    ROOM SURVEILLANCE SYSTEM**
Offers a longer transmission range. Consists of an SK2 room
transmitter and AR1 receiver in a presentation case.

**KIT THREE ROOM SURVEILLANCE SYSTEM**
**(MAINS OPERATED)**
For long term monitoring. Consists of an MT4 mains transmitter
and an AR1 receiver in a presentation case.

**KIT FOUR   TELEPHONE SURVEILLANCE SYSTEM**
Consists of an SKT2 telephone transmitter and an AR1
receiver in a presentation case.

straightforward to install. The
adaptor and socket will function
in their normal capacity and are
inconspicuous. The mains
transmitter is compact and is
suitable for installation within
existing fittings or appliances.

**Matco Inc.**, www.mat-co.com. 800-440-0299. No printed catalog, maybe no fixed address, Matco seems to buy surplus or overruns of Asian security equipment and then resells them in small parcels.

Board cameras, complete systems, 2.4 GHz transmitter/receiver combos for as little as $89.00 (in lots of 100, price goes up as quantity drops).

**Micro** 5A Parson Street, Hendon, London NW4 1QA United Kingdom www. microelec.com. "Suppliers to Her Majesty's Government". Importers of Cony Japanese bugs and taps, modified Sony recorders, pen transmitters and pinhole cameras.

More expensive than their Asian OEM cousins, but a real source for hard to get items.

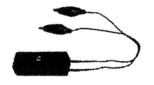

**Spooktech.com** "listening devices, hidden cameras, background searching, telephone devices". They would not give out a physical address, nor return a phone call to inquire about same...

FREQUENCY UHF 398-399MHZ 3 CHANNEL TRANSMITTING RANGE300 OVER METERS

| TKS-120 | TKS-121 | TKS-122 | TKS-123 | TKS-124 |
|---|---|---|---|---|
| LONG DISTANCE TYPE | PEN TYPE | CALCULATOR TYPE | CRUAK-THROUGH TYPE | MAINS MODULE TYPE |
| 66×27×14MM | 14×130MM | 102×75×30MM | 66×27×14MM | 41×15×13MM |

**Suma Designs** The Workshops 95 Main Road, Near Atherstone, Warwickshire, CV9 2LE England. Suma only produces kits; but man, oh man, are they *kits*...

For the last 13 years they have designed, developed and marketed some units that match the CIA in sheer sophistication. The "common" units can be received on the commercial radio band or tuned to go above into more secure public service bands.

But the real stuff comes in the form of animals that aren't found in the normal zoo.

Know what I mean?

The voice activated VXT drains its batteries at a mere 2mA when in the standby mode, then kicks into gear when noise above a set threshold is passed, bringing the transmitter to full power (about 25 hours continuous).

Time on and trigger level adjustable. About 20 pounds sterling, or add another $25 for a completely assembled and tested model...

Other favorites include – SCLX subcarrier transmitter which requires a special subcarrier decoder to demod the signal (also available from SUMA) making it very, very hard to find, much less overhear. RCTX remote controlled transmitter that only switches on for preset period when the operator activates its remote signaling transmitter. Average "on period" is about 2 minutes, but every time you push the little button another 2 minutes is added.

This is almost-CIA level stuff at Wal Mart prices.

**Kudelski S.A.** CH-1033 Cheseaux/Lausane, Switzerland. OEM of the Nagra tape recorder line.

Still the state-of-the-art in surveillance and high end commercial recording.

# NAGRA SNST

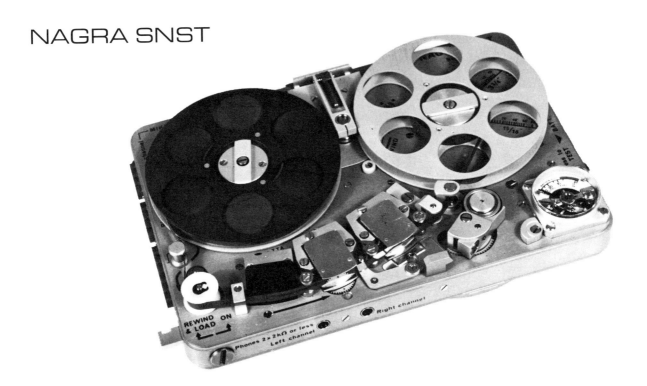

**Adaptive Digital Systems, Inc. Irvine, CA.** Is now marketing the next generation of surreptitious recording paraphernalia, specifically the Eagle and the Fbird8

Look at the specs:

- Radio/microphone logging
- Telephone/fax monitoring
- VOX, auto or manual
- Caller ID, tone an pulse reading
- SVGA Display with touch tone
- Field expandable from 8 to 128 channels

All this is enclosed in a 4.4 x 2.5 unit powered by 2 AAA batteries that records 2.5 hours (5+ on the Eagle 2) of digital audio.

The unit will record on almost any digital media including CD ROM. This means one can duplicate the Data (on CD) for under $2.00 a copy, send them to one s friends, relatives, local cops, distant cops, NCIC, well, whatever.

Tiny, efficient, digital, far cheaper than the Nagra entries, showing the shape of things to come. I would assume not, title 3, meaning you can probably buy one.

# LASER WINDOW BOUNCE LISTENER SYSTEMS

USES SCATTERED SECONDARY REFLECTIONS!

Remarkable concept allows user to hear sounds within a premise over a beam of laser light reflected from a window or similar surface. Experimental device provides hours of interesting and educational use. Utilizes a visible red laser that simplifys alignment and discourages illegal use. Usable range will vary-expect about 20 to 50 feet. Optional lens will increase range 200 to 400 feet! Further range requires expensive optics. Caution-check local law in your state if planning to use for accessing oral communication.

System setup shown using scattered reflection method

**RECEIVER:** CYLINDERICAL ENCLOSURE BUILT IN VOICE FILTER ULTRA LOW NOISE DESIGN 9 VOLT BATTERY WITH HEADPHONES

**LWB5** Plans All Systems..**$20.00**   **LWB5K** KIT/PLANS...............**$149.50**
**LWB50** Assmbld Laser and Receiver..(req video tripod).........**$199.50**

**LASER:** SELECTED FOR COHERENCE 4+mw @650nm visible red BATTERY OPERATED 6 hrs

**LWB70** Delux System-Sold For Experimental Purposes Only.....................................$299.50

USES SCATTERED REFLECTIONS FROM WINDOWS SURFACE. ELIMINATES PROBLEMS OF ESTABLISHING TWO POSITIONS REQUIRED WHEN USING REAL REFLECTIONS. INCLUDES RECEIVER AND HIGH BRIGHTNESS LASER GUN SIGHT MOUNTED TOGETHER. REQUIRES ALIGNMENT BY USER.

## Information Unlimited

POB 716, Amherst, NH 03031 www.amazing1.com. Not specifically a surveillance supplier, IU never-the-less has a very interesting selection of goods for the covert minded. Many of the choices are kits (real kits) some can be purchased in a fully assembled format.

I can personally testify to the design and execution of IU's products – they are owned by an electronics engineer I've talked to many times and I've had nothing but success with his product.

You should have this catalog and probably a few of the items just for the proverbial rainy day.

# 6 TRANSMITTER Project Kits

CAUTION: Check Public Law 90-352

## $UPER VALUE $ALE

1 Super Sensitive Ultra Clear 1Mile+ Voice Transmitter
2 1 Mile + Telephone Transmitter
3 Telephone "DROP IN" Transmitter Line Powered- Needs No Batteries!!
4 Tracking/Homing Beacon "Beeping Transmitter"
5 Transmitter Rebroadcasts Video or Audio Outputs
6 Short Range TV/FM Disrupter NEAT PRANK!!! Discretion Advised

**All 6 Above Kits Plus FREE Info Data Pack on "HELPFUL HINTS" Using Wireless Devices**

COMBOX Kits and Plans....................$59.50

## 3mi FM VOICE XMTR

Subminiature crystal clear, hear a pin drop!! Excellent for home security, monitoring of invalids or children near open water and other hazards. Become the neighborhood disk jockey. Works with any standard FM broadcast radio.

Operates 3 to 18 Volts. Tuneable Over Standard FM Broadcast. Many Useful Home Security Applications. Easy to assemble- Great for a science project.

FMV1 Plans....................$7.00
FMV1K Kit/Plans.........$39.50

# CYBERNETIC EAR!

Use For Courtesy Lowering of TV Volume Control etc. Detect Rattles and Other Mechanic Abnomalies, Leaking Gases, Air, or Electrical Corona. Excellent Safety Aid For Shop or Lab.

Enhances Hearing 3 to 4 Times
Adjustable Volume Control
Built In Long Lasting Batteries

CYBEREAR Ready to Use...................$19.95

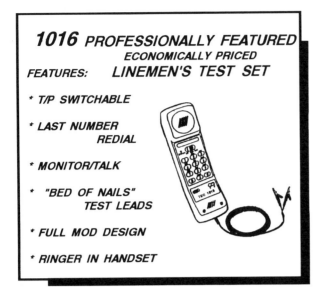

## 1016 PROFESSIONALLY FEATURED
### ECONOMICALLY PRICED
FEATURES: **LINEMEN'S TEST SET**

* T/P SWITCHABLE

* LAST NUMBER REDIAL

* MONITOR/TALK

* "BED OF NAILS" TEST LEADS

* FULL MOD DESIGN

* RINGER IN HANDSET

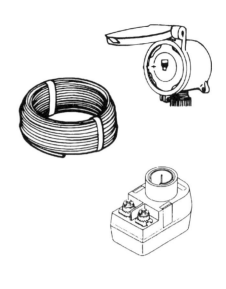

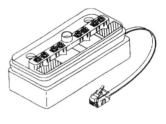

**Show Time Products** 3600 Gus Thomasson Ste. 162, Mesquite, TX 75150. Top level, FBI oriented super sophisticated room transmitter. 1-300 $15.00 each, for really nosy people $12.95 in quantities over 300...

### SPY SIZE

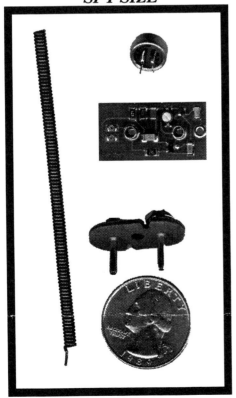

**Telephone Extension Corp.** 82 E. Central Ave., Pearl River, NY 10965. Reseller of, you guessed it, telephone "accessories". Selection includes long play recorder, DTMF detector, Hold Invader and "monitor" phones (see Shomer-Tec) but their real strength is a bunch of slightly marked up real telephone stuff, i.e., lineman's handset, tone generators, plugs, selector switches. Add a couple of low end "voice changers" and you've pretty much got it.

_**NO**_ Soldering Required

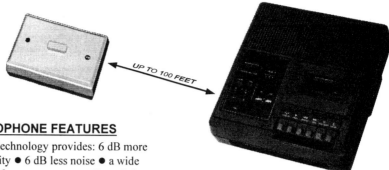

UP TO 100 FEET

**Omnicron Electronics** POB 623, Putnam, CT 06260. OEM suppliers of extra long play recorders, many designed for multi channel police dispatch type recording, some for "covert" use.

Also have a nice selection of phone adapters, unusual pressure microphone and other supplies. Recorders known for their reliability and professional construction.

## MICROPHONE FEATURES

PZM® technology provides: 6 dB more sensitivity ● 6 dB less noise ● a wide smooth frequency response free of phase interference ● consistent pickup anywhere around the mic ● Built-in amplifier, rolls off frequencies below the voice range to reduce rumble from machinery, air conditioning, etc. ● Because of its tailored frequency response and PZM® construction, it picks up conversations with extra clarity ● Designed for room monitoring with Omnicron VR series recorders, it looks like a wall switch not a microphone ● Can be mounted in a ceiling or wall using a standard electrical outlet box ● Supplied with 20' microphone to recorder cable and a 25' extension cable ● Additional extension cables are available ● 1 year limited warranty.

## RECORDER FEATURES

Powerful 2-watt RMS amplifier for crisp, clear, distortion-free sound ● ¼" Jack for use with PZ-2L microphone, provides for audio connection and power ● 3.5mm Jacks for external standard microphone and auxiliary audio source ● ¼" External Speaker Jack ● Four ¼" Headphone Jacks ● Bar graph record level indicator ● Automatic Tape Stop and power shut-off in all modes ● Full Range Volume and Tone Controls ● Pause Control instantly stops tape ● Public Address cability to monitor external audio at any time, with on/off switch and LED indicator ● 2X ANSI Digital Tape Counter ● 3-Prong Attached AC Power Cord ● Retractable Carrying Handle ● Supplied with one MLC-120 Cassette Tape ● 1 year limited warranty.

## *Telephone Supervisory Adapters*

With a **TSA** adapter and your VLR recorder you will record all conversations on one telephone instrument. The TSA connects to the handset or headset jack on your telephone.

**TSA-3** Handset Adapter

The TSA-3 provides an inexpensive way to connect your logging recorder so that it can monitor both sides of all conversations which take place on the handset or headset of a telephone. Only conversations which take place on that one telephone instrument will be recorded. It can be used on any telephone that has a standard four slot modular handset jack, single line or multi-line, analog or digital. It does not affect the operation of your phone and can be easily self-installed between the handset jack and handset cord.

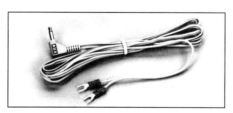

**AUX-6S** Auxiliary Audio Source Direct Input Cable

The AUX-6S auxiliary input cable is used to connect your VLR Voice Logging Recorder to audio sources which do not require isolation (two-way radios, scanners, other recorders, etc.). The 6' cable has a 3.5mm mini-phone plug on one end to match the AUX jack on the VLR recorder and spade lug terminals on the other end for connection to your audio source. It is also available to match specific requirements with many different styles of connectors and comes in lengths to match your exact needs.

**International Logistics Systems, Inc.,** 234 McLean Blvd., Patterson, NJ 07504. A nice mix of legal audio (body wires, recorders, etc.) hidden video, scramblers, DTMF decoders, shock batons, personal document shredders, night scopes, this and that.

Prices in line with general suppliers, nice selection.

## CONFERENCE ROOM MONITORING SYSTEM #6605

A total security system which allows you to record conferences. Visible or discreet microphones gather all audio and relay it to a central recorder. Unit doubles as an alarm system which alerts you when someone enters the room without authorization. Simple installation. Optional video signals can be recorded.

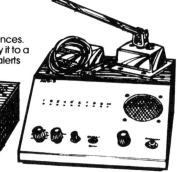

## TELE-EAR #14100

Remote activation feature allows the user to telephone from virtually anywhere in the world and listen to a break-in or emergency at another location. A sensitive microphone detects the faintest sounds, ranging from hushed conversations, to a water faucet left running, all with excellent clarity. Includes detailed instructions, remote beeper and a detachable microphone.

## VIDEO ATTACHE SYSTEM #5580

This system, enclosed in an attractive high quality leather case records both audio and video on a 8MM recorder with flip up screen, which is used for setup or instant playback. The video signal is gathered by a low light level CCD camera attached to a pinhole lens. A super sensitive microphone with separate amplifier guarantees sound reproduction in the most demanding environments.
This system can be manually activated or by a remote transmitter.

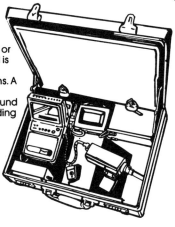

## AUTOMATIC TELEPHONE ANALYZER #4740

Tests telephones single or multi-line. Performs 120 individual tests on multi-line phones in less than twenty minutes. This unit is non-alerting and does all wire comparisons.
Capable of testing electronic and conventional phones.

Completely self-contained with all accessories, adaptors for all telephones. Carrying case and instructions. AC powered

## EXECUTIVE ATTACHE SHOCKER CASE #14293

All features of #14250 plus motion sensing deterrent, fine belt leather, audio alert for arm/disarm.

## PORTABLE VOICE SCRAMBLER #3110

From simple monitoring to sophisticated bugs and tapes, this unit protects your conversation at both ends.
Totally self contained, usable worldwide on any telephone: office, cellular phones, home portable phones, without modification.
Over 52,000 code combinations, offers highest security of any unit in its price range. 9V powered. Easy to use.

Direction Technology, Inc. represents several companies that provide theFederal, State, Local Law Enforcement and Military community with variousproducts that are used for surveillance. Unfortunately, due to thenature of these products, we are unable to exhibit detailed descriptionsat this site. Should you need detailed information, please contactus via our email and we will contact you. A generic listing of theseproducts is included below:

Miniature radio transmitters<br>
Audio Surveillance interception/recording systems<br>
Remote activated audio/video surveillance systems<br>
Ultrasonic microphones<br>
Computer Keyboard interception/re-transmission system<br>
Cellular Monitoring/Interception system<br>
Cellular Telephone based listening device<br>
Body worn transmitters<br>
Surveillance Platforms, Camper Tops, Vans, modules<br>
Portable Wide Band Audio Receiver Kits<br>
Portable Video Surveillance System<br>
Portable Video Motion Recorder System<br>
Audio & Video Attaché Case<br>
"MIDNITEYES" Ultra Low Light IR Sensitive Color Camcorder<br>
Portable 12 vdc Power Supply<br>
Audio Processor and Distribution System<br>
Pin Hole Lens, CCD Board 1/3" Cameras<br>
Portable Miniature Board Camera Kit<br>
Vehicle "Remote Disable" System<br>
Send Us Your Comments

Direction Technology, Inc.<br>
PO Box 911<br>
Centreville, Virginia 20122-0911<br>
Or call us:<br>
Tel: (703) 222-6275 Fax: (703) 222-9897

---

**Private Eye Enterprises Inc.**, 4289 Beltline Rd., Addison, TX 75244 www.pidallas.com. Dialed number recorders, video cameras hidden in the usual array of things we all love to hide video cameras in.

Night vision, video transmitters, Prices on the high end of the spectrum.

**Canwood Products** POB 585 Beumont, CA 92223. Minimal line to avoid putting the customer thru the nightmare of too many choices.

**HDS, Inc.** 12310 Pinecrest Rd., Suite 300 Reston VA 20191. HDS (Household Data Services has been a primary OEM supplier for all manners of Federal, State, Local and International cops (or agents, sorry FBI).

They do not and will not sell to any non-law enforcement folks so just sort of including them for the process of comparison.

Figure audio bugs up to and including the $1,000 range, nifty video products and God knows what else up to and including, well let's just say plan on taking out that second mortgage...

# SYSTEM "65"
## Remote Controlled Surveillance System

**Remote Control of:**
- Pan left/right
- Tilt up/down
- Zoom in/out
- Focus near/far
- Power (Transmitter & Camera) on/off

## MINI TELEPHONE RECORDER

This device is similar to the Tele-150 above but is much smaller and is equipped with a pair of alligator clips for fast connection anywhere along a telephone line. This device will start and stop any recorder automatically and records both sides of the conversation. Use this with our long play recorders for out of sight extended recording. Size is 1" x 1/2" Requires no battery.

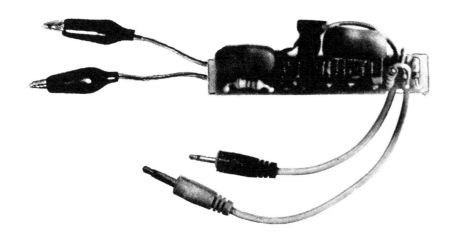

**Protector Enterprises** POB 520294, Salt Lake City, UT 84152. Strictly a reseller they actually choose their gear pretty well and don't add horrendous markups. A little audio, bunch o' video stuff, Dan Gibson parabolic, a few Japanese imports, Capri Electronics, etc.

Worth looking into, good pricing structure.

**Rainbow Kits** 6227 Coffman Rd., Indianapolis, IN 46268 www.rainbowkits.com. Some very low priced tap/bug kits (I mean *really* low priced) plus a bunch of OPS as well as an item or two I'm not sure where she be coming from...

# Press a button and learn every number dialed on your phone while you were away!

Stores the last 490 digits it receives.
Connects to a phone, scanner, amateur radio, or etc.
Decodes any DTMF signal transmitted.

## MICRO-MINIATURE PHONE TRANSMITTER

We haven't seen a smaller phone transmitter than the MMPT2 kit. Powered by the phone, it requires no battery. Transmits both sides of a phone conversation to an FM radio up to a 1/4 mile away. Tunable from 88 to 108MHz FM. Attach it to one phone or add it to the line to pick up all incoming calls. The MMPT2 is undetectable if properly installed. The kit is made with surface mounted parts, we have already mounted these parts. You install the leaded parts.
SIZE: .45" x .6"
MMPT2                                         KIT **$29.95**

**AMC Sales** 193 Vaquero Dr., Boulder, CO 80303 www.siteleader.com/cat alogdepot/AMCSC-home. AMC lived in the "gadget" ads in magazines like Popular Science since I was a, well, let's just say a lot younger. They're still around offering OPS at bargain basement prices.

VOX recorder starter under $30.00, phone scramblers and one of the only pen registers (number dialed recorder) still available.

## Features:

- Registers user dialing number, duration of call, charge of call, counter number when phone in use.
- Registers information up to 1200 sets of calls.
- Printer device prints out information
- 16-digit LCD displays information.
- Calendar and time of day display.
- Security pass code protects information read-out.
- Restricts long-distance calls, duration of call, charge of call, and free calls used.
- Code number control without key.
- Message meter for incoming calls.
- Tone/Pulse system compatible.
- Can store 5 sets of long-distance numbers.
- Can store 40 sets of different chargeable units.
- Calculates the charge of each call.
- 9 volt battery not supplied.

**Ramsey Electronics** 793 Canning Parkway, Victor, NY 14564 www.ramseyelectronics.com. One of the better kept secrets in the biz, RE does not sell surveillance gear per se, and make no cute little hints about "articles to be placed in the bedroom"; they do, however, offer some of the lowest priced, functional "items of interest" on the US market.

Many of their items are kits, but easily constructed kits (not "attach one wire", but simple for anyone with some assembly background), Ramsey has pulled some of their product line to match the changing laws and enforcement thereof. Might want to buy a few things while still available...

Two very nice pieces to have in the old kit would be the SS-70A speech scrambler/descrambler (fully assembled for less than $80.00) which will ungibberize speech inversion systems such as those used on cheaper wireless (non-spread spectrum) phone systems, police department transmissions, some scrambled bugs, etc., and a #25.00 FM receiver that is designed for out-of-band tuning. This feature allows one to set the frequency of any FM bug/tap above or below the commercial FM band.

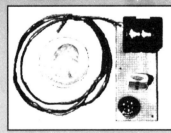

**Intelpro Co., Worldwide Headquarters**, 616 Cedar Hill Drive, Suite 1034, Allentown, PA 18103www.intel.pro.net. These nice folks have, in an attempt to circumvent the US laws devised a way to build (or buy) real surveillance goodies from "countries not of the US".

They will take your order BUT WILL NOT DELIVER INSIDE THE USA. So what good does this do you? There are at least three worldwide mail drop directories on the market as we speak who, will, for a small payment, collect and forward your mail to you sans incriminating return address.

Or, of course if you have a friend, relative, ex-college roomie (who skipped to Canada, or stayed in Thailand) ask for a little favor.

The following items from this section are build Outside of United States of America.
This items are Restricted and cannot be shipped to USA. (**No exceptions**)
Allows up to four weeks prior shipping from Outside of USA to your Country.

PEN BUG
PAGER BUG
VIDEO TAPE BUG
SOCKETS BUG
CD COVER
MARLBORO BUG
ANY PURPOSE BUG

**Browse and Buy** This is an internet only company which seems to have pretty fair prices although not a huge selection. wwwbrowseandbuy.com.

**Paradigm Advanced Technologies** 1 Concord Globe #201, Don Mills, Ont M3C 3NG Canada. PAT is touting some very nice, very new surveillance gear in their press releases. They were a start up company last year and have reported sales of $500,000 in this year's financial statement.

PAT offers a Digital Video Recorder (DVR) that will record, store and playback high resolution black and white or color images in the same fashion as a timelapse VCR (video cassette recorder for security applications). The main difference, is that it is a computerized version of a Timelapse VCR that operates exactly like a PC and is Windows based.

Or take the Peek-a-View, a low cost version of Videobank DVR, essentially a shrink wrap product, consisting of software and a small 3"x3" device that plugs onto the parallel port of any computer.

Their R3 system is a mobile video surveillance system which enables the operator (sitting at his distant computer) management to track listen and view in real time mobile targets including people, vehicles or "inventory".

The unit can apparently be stashed on the target and then initiated by the operator or by any number of on-site triggers. At this point the unit, via cellular transmitters broadcasts not only GPS location data but real time video and audio.

# R-3
## Video Bank with GPS Technology

As a company whose focus is in the area of digital video management systems it was only natural to take the technology to the next stage of development. The R-3 system is a system unparalleled in the market today. There have been great strides in GPS application development as previously mentioned. However, Paradigm is in the unique position to bring to market the first ever GPS tracking system capable of storing and transmitting video to a remote monitoring station for the purposes of identifying a person or event. In addition to video, will be the two-way audible link enabling the monitoring station to listen in to event. Essentially, by implementing an imbedded PC, we have integrated Videobank and a GPS tracking system with audio and video capabilities. Paradigm has acquired unique GPS transponding and mapping software as an integral component of the new product to be offered. The actual cost using a fully functional embedded PC is less than the desktop version.

The R3 system is a mobile video surveillance system which enables an operator in a monitoring station to track listen and view in real time, mobile targets, such as vehicles, people, or inventory. The images obtained, can be used to provide valuable evidence of any unsafe or illegal operation.

The system incorporates the full functionality of Paradigm's proprietary Video8ank DVR software. This will allow for recording, transmission, as well as total interactive capabilities enabling an operator at a remote monitoring station to turn down the vehicle. The system utilizes frame by frame positioning information provided by a Navistar GPS sensor, information that will allow the display of the video on a digitized map to localize where the event is happening with accuracy within a several meter radius.

After the friendly feds came down with a vengeance on anything with the word "spy" in it most spy, shops, factories, stories, emporiums took the not too subtle hint and flew the coop.

There are a few left around and you can fell free to check their offerings although most either charge extensively for a catalog (CCS being a good case in point) or have gone strictly on-line.

A few won't even give out their addresses. Check out my selections, go your favorite search engine and check out "spy", "secret", "bugs, "taps, etc.

Note many of the selections are quite redundant (well again with the exception of CCS' "remote controlled night vision submarine").

CCS can be found at www.spyzone.com, under CounterSpy shops in various cities and as LEEC.

The FAX manager II is the file cabinet of the 90's. It automatically stores copies of every fax sent and received from your office fax machine on a DAT (Digital Audio Tape).

It logs any number of pages in real time and can capture information transmitted at any speed for 300 to 9600 bits per second.

It prints high-resolution images on a specially modified fax machine.

**Incognito Services**, www.incognitoservices.com. did not return our call for a physical address so I will tell you their number seems to be 650-363-9100. They have been around a while, have a good rep and seem to be in-line price wise.

Our agency designs, builds, sells and maintains covert video equipment primarily used for the apprehension of video evidence. This special or customized equipment is used by licensed private investigators; some law enforcement agencies and legitimate business owners concerned about protecting their buildings, offices, assets, etc. The modern video camera can be as small as a postage stamp and can be quite conveniently hidden in practically anything. We have in stock and ready to use the following devices. Wall clock camera; wall mirror camera; desk telephone camera; men's tie camera; child's stuffed toy camera; complete fanny pack camera and recorder; VCR with built in video camera. We are available for consulting or special equipment projects. Some video equipment rentals are available for technically qualified clients. Voice access 650-363-9100 extension 95.

Covert video equipment installations by experienced and qualified technicians is a specialty. We have access to all commercially available video equipment and specialty devices for security CCTV. Custom built projects and equipment installations are easily designed with specific applications in mind.

Since 1980, our professional staff of licensed engineers, C7 contractors, video technicians and experienced countermeasures personnel have provided quality services throughout California the west coast and western Canada.

For example, a simple miniaturized black and white video camera can cost as little as $275.00. However, should it be necessary to have the camera pre-wired for immediate use or permanently installed in an item such as a man's tie or child's stuffed toy, the price will increase commensurately. Contact our staff at 650-363-9100 extension 95 for details or e-mail to us at **video@incognitoservices.com**.

# Quality and Performance You Can Trust!

Model T-220

Model T-420

Model C-510
Cosmetic Accessory Line

Model R-300

The "R" series can record a 20 db whisper at over 100 feet away from the source.

Model R-310

Our T-220 series surveillance briefcase line is equipped with audio and video/2.4 GHz transmission and simultaneous built-in time/dated recorder options. The T-420 starts around $495.00. The "C" series is a cosmetic accessory line for women offering compacts, lipstick, etc. with built-in 100 and 300 milli-watts audio/video transmitters. The "R" series from TRIDELTA consists of extremely powerful audio transmission and intercept devices concealed in common ink pens, pagers, calculators, electrical outlets, surge suppressors and many other items. The "R" series is a restricted series and sold to Law Enforcement and Government agencies only.

Sold to Federal, State, Local Law Enforcement, Government Agencies, and duly licensed Private Investigative Companies ONLY. Not for sale to the general public.

**Tridelta Technologies, Inc.** 2217 Princess Anne St., Suite 305, Fredericksburg, VA 22401 www.trideltagroup.com. This multifaceted firm features equipment as well as training and actual operatives for those in the need. Very nice selection of men's suits (Pierre Cardin, Bill Blass, etc.) with built in cameras, recorders, body wires or countermeasures goodies built-in.

And for about the same price Needless Markup sells the suit without any unusual components. Exact suit measurements must be supplied with order.

Also some nice gear (title 3 for law folk only, others for other) in both the surveillance and countermeasures fields.

Tridelta claims they can produce just about anything required up to and including unmanned surveillance aircraft.

**You Have to see it to believe it!** The new M-909 from Sony has all the features of other long-play micro recorders housed in an extremely small package. In fact, it's 2-3/4" (w) x 2-5/8" (h) x 3/4" (d) and weights in at only 3.6 oz. including battery. This tiny unit is the perfect "body wire" because it can be conceled just about anywhere, in a cigarette pack, a shirt or suit pocket, pants pocket or purse. It even comes with a tie-clip mic with pause control switch. Features include: Adjustable Voice-Activation, Auto-Reverse for 3 full hours of continuous recording, earphone jack, sound level equalizer and excellent sound reproduction.

**Security Trade Surveillance & Countersurveillance Company** 6065 Hillcroft Suite 413, Houston, TX 77081 www.wwsites.com/tx/securitytrade. Resellers Panasonic, JBC, Silver Creek, Capri, a couple of Asian covert cameras, auto start recorders, etc.

Surprisingly prices in line.

DTI Surveillance Products, Direction Technology, Inc., POB 911, Centreville, VA 20122 www.directionfinder.com. Can't think of much to add to this listing...

# Surveillance Equipment

I-OR-US-4-U-SPY 3414 S. Cooper, #107, Arlington, TX 76015."Special Products For You - State the the art tapeing (sic) devices". No catalog, stole our logo, but, hell, who knows, might be great people...

**Electronic Equipment Bank** 323 Mill St., Vienna, VA 22180, www.access.digex.net/~eeb/eeb.html. Full spectrum communications supplies for ICOM receivers, scanners, 2 ways, antennas etc.

Good prices, great selection they even rent some products. Also see their entry in the electronic surveillance section.

**Total Point Inc.,** 311 Black St., Whitehorse, Yukon Canada Y1A 2N1, . OEM of briefcase size FM transmitters that kick out 5 watts on the commercial FM band. Idea here is, record the message, set it up and it blocks out other signals. Used for bear activity alerts (Boy Scout honor), could be used for a number of other purposes...

# MICRO 30
## Micro with data/time stamp

Now you'll know when the tape you're playing was recorded. While you record, the year, month, day and time are digitally encoded on the tape each minute and shown on the LCD display during playback. MICRO has two speeds, quick-record, fast-play, index marker, built-in microphone with adjustable sensitivity and earphone jack. Requirtes 2 "AA" batteries or power AC adapter.

## $109.95

# TCD-D8
## SONY'S NEWEST DAT PLAYER/RECORDER

Second generation technology brings you the new TCD-D8 portable digital audio tape recorder. Backlit LCD keeps you on topof all the features. 4 hour play mode, auto date and manual/auto recording levels are just a few features of the TCD-D8.

## $699.95

# World's Smallest Scanner

Need a sensitive ccanner powerful enough to receive weak signals, yet no bigger tha a pack of cigarettes? The AR16 will have a major impact in the scanner market. Anticipated for government and other authorized users as early as Nov. "96 with FCC approved units expected for '97 release. (FCC prohibits sale of this unit to non-qualified buyers prior to FCC approval.

This compact scanner will include standard AOR features such as RS232 computer control, 500 memory channels, super sensitivity and much more. The reaction tune capability, when connected to the Scout is expected to exceed the performance of the popular AR8000/Scout combinations.

*AR16*
*EXPECTED PRICE RANGE*
*$300.00*

## TA-BF101

FUNCTIONS:

. Record any incoming facsimile message and re-send to destination fax machine automatically.

. Can be remotely controlled by any other fax machine to receive recorded fax messages（can store up to 30 pages of A4 size fax messages）.

FUNCTIONS

. Monitor calls on all nearby cell sites:
  - Locking Monitor:Can store up to 20 cellular phone numbers
                     for auto search, locking monitoring.
  - Random Monitor: Can lock monitoring any nearby cellphone
                     conversations and show the phone number
                     on the screen.
. Can be connected to the Voice activated recorder〔ATR-RQ.L
  307（VAS）〕to record the conversation content, corresponding
  time and dialing number.
. Available for AMPS, ETACS system.

**Tronic Ace Technology, Inc.** 4th floor, No. 6 Alley 3, Lane 117 Sanmin Rd., Hsintien, Taipei, Taiwan ROC. Yes, our old friends in the Republic Of offer some very nice, very low priced surveillance units, low end countermeasures and "accessories".

I also like the fact that they work out of an alley, provides a true sense of surreptitious shopping.

Good (well, great for the money) audio video transmitters, ("can receive talking meeting conversations – different designs square box") both in "general" (VHF) and "professional" (UHF) models with varying power outputs. Nice cell phone grabber and fax tap...

Same equipment soon to be seen in other catalogs for much more money.

Might want to deal directly with their sales manager – Mohamed Ali. Really.

Continued on next page

. Can receive meeting / concert both audio and video signals from 3,000 up to 15,000 meters away.
. SHF high efficiency transmitter and receiver to assure high performance.

. VIDEO: M/NTSC, B/PAL, G/PAL
. MODULATION: FM
. VIDEO OUTPUT: negative
. TX/RX FREQ: 1150 - 1350MHz
. FREQ. ALIGNMENT: synthesizer or crystal oscillator
. TX OUTPUT POWER: 0.5W  ( TA-BV105SHF )
                                    2.0W  ( TA-BV120SHF )

**Silver Creek Industries, Inc.** POB 1988 Manitowoc, WI 54221. SC manufacturers the original "bionic ear" (not to mention the BE booster) sold in many low end gadget catalogs. They have expanded their line to include a series of amplified headsets for hunting, or just listening that amplify sound up to 800% with an auto loud noise cutoff feature.

Order direct and save...

Action Ear® Sport

*Tan-camo*  *Black-camo*

*Our Premier Amplifier*

Bionic Ear® Scout

*Exceptional Value*

Bionic Ear® and Booster®

*The Original*

### A. SONY NT-1 DIGITAL RECORDER SYSTEM

The Sony NT-1 has to be the smallest, high resolution recorder on the market today. This recorder actually records onto a digital tape for the highest quality playback ever. The tapes themselves are no bigger than a postage stamp and can record for up to 120 minutes per side. The recorder features a built-in clock/calendar that records the date and time at the beginning of any recording. Calendar records up to the year 2099. The unit comes complete with AC adapter connection, connecting cord, stereo microphone and stand, microphone attenuator, 90 minute NT cassette tape, stereo headphone and carry case. This recorder is used by most federal agencies for their undercover operations because of its incredible sound quality.

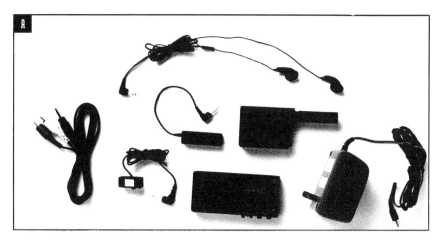

**Spy Headquarters** 125 East Northern Ave., Phoenix, AZ 85020. After the great spy shop busts most closed their doors and wandered off into the sunset, or, in some cases, jail. A few dropped the offense materials and stayed in business.

Such is SH. Large catalog of others people's stuff; Dan Gibson mics, pepper spray, extended play recorders, covert video, handcuffs, lockpicks, recording briefcases, Tele-Monitor 2000, batons, a couple of useful countermesures items fake "novelty" bombs and, guess what?

Prices are not too bad! Definitely not the usual 800% "has the word spy in the title" markup.

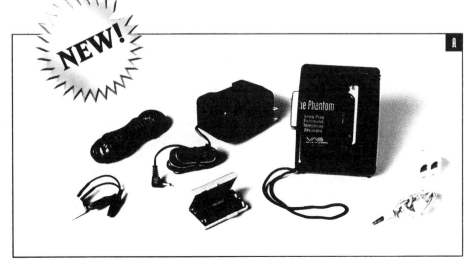

### A. PHANTOM TELEPHONE RECORDER

For high quality, long play telephone recording in a sub-compact unit, the Phantom gets the job done. Eight hours (4 per side) of recording on a single D-140 tape. Because of its voice activated circuit, the tape only runs when conversation is present on the line. When used on a single line phone, both sides of the conversation are clearly recorded from any and all extensions. Since all the electronics are built into the unit, there are no bulky control or interface couplers to hassle with. System is powered for 22 hours on fully charged batteries or can operate indefinitely on included AC power adapter. System includes, modular connector cable, AC power adapter\recharger, NiCad batteries, C140 tape and duplex phone adapter. Measures 4.5"x3.25"x1.375".

You, as an astute observer, will note the similarity of some of the featured goods to other Asian "manufactuers". My best guess is that SM buys some items from the same OEM's that other surveillance suppliers do and produces a few of their own to compliant the line.

At any rate; here one can find taps, bugs, thru wall (actually, as do I, these guys seem to have a fetish with this aspect) amplifiers, pinhole mics, fiber optics, and other tools of the trade.

Definately compare specs and prices before ordering from other suppliers.

**Spectrum Communications Corp.** 1055 W. Germantown Pike, Norristown, PA 19403. Complete audio surveillance systems as well as individual amplifier boards, antennas, receivers. Professional gear, good reputation. (System shown About $2,500).

# *HIGH POWER/HIGH PERFORMANCE/LONG RANGE*
# RADIO SURVEILLANCE SYSTEM

### For Drug Enforcement & Other Surveillance Operations

**The Spectrum Surveillance System was designed to meet the demand for High Performance/High Quality Radio Surveillance equipment with longer range, less interference and better audio quality than previously available units.** These versatile units provide many new and unique features. The Body Transmitter features high power, excellent audio with internal or external mics, and a "Quick-Change" 9V Battery. The battery is easily replaced by pushing in on the spring-loaded tabs. This releases the battery. *There's no fumbling with the usual clip or wires.* If the battery is accidentally reversed, the red LED illuminates, and the transmitter will not be damaged.

**The SR250 Receiver is a very High Performance Portable/Desktop unit** — very similar to the one used in Spectrum long range repeaters. It is far superior to common "Scanners" or "Handi Talkies." A Gell Cell Battery is built-in and does not have the same problems as NICAD batteries — such as "memory effects", etc. A Signal Strength/Battery Meter is included, as well as a large Speaker, Audio Filters, Output Jack to recorder, and red LEDs for Power and "Carrier Detect".

Spectrum has over 1 ½ decades of experience in two-way radio equipment, and we use only the finest quality designs, components, and workmanship — *for years of reliable service.*

### SS100 BRIEFCASE SYSTEM INCLUDES
■ SR250 Receiver      ■ 1 Body Transmitter      ■ Miniature Lapel Mic
■ Cassette Tape Recorder With 1 Tape      ■ Rcvr. Whip Antenna
■ Receiver-Recorder Hookup Cable      ■ AC Power Module for Recorder
■ Receiver AC Power Cable. 12 VDC Power Cable With Cigarette Lighter Plug
■ Recorder Earphone      ■ Foam-lined Briefcase

**Complete Briefcase Portable System**

**Chinet Spy Shop** 250 Portland Road, Hove, Sussex, BN3 5Qt Ukwww.chinet.uk. Push themselves as a big supplier of "forbidden" gear, but most is minor Japanese stuff at 3-4 times the original price.

One Exception would be the remote garage and car alarm duplicator. Not sure where this comes from.

**Transmitter duplication system is used to copy remote door openers or car alarms.**

**Carl's Electronics** POB 182 Sterling, MA 01564 wwwelectronickits.com. A number of inexpensive plans and a few kits for low end surveillance and counter measures units.

# CK202 - FM TELEPHONE TRANSMITTER

Miniature transmitter attaches in series to your telephone line, transmits the conversation 3/4 of a mile and more to an FM receiver. Tunable to a clear spot in the FM band of your radio. Completely parasitic; i.e. uses the power from the telephone line and needs no battery. The circuit might be used to share or record conversations, but not intended for illegal use.

Hosfelt Electronics, Inc., 2700 Sunset Blvd., Stubenville, OH 43952. General electronics plus very low priced board cameras, hook up wire, coax, and hidden cameras.

## PASSIVE INFRARED CAMERA

Camera lens

Mfg. - PROVIDEO
5" x 2-7/8" x 2-5/16"
Fully operational passive infrared motion sensor designed to detect movement in any area while simultaneously recording an event. 3.6mm wide angle pinhole lens with electronic auto iris. .5 lux minimum illumination. 400 lines of resolution. Video output - RCA jack. PIR instruction sheet included. Powered by 12 VDC adapter (included).

Alltronics 2300 Zanker Rd., San Jose, CA 95131 www.alltronics.com. Electronic components, a few low end transmitters, STAMP computer kits.

### FM WIRELESS MIKE KIT
Powerful two-stage, wireless mike kit transmits over half mile (up to 1Km in the open). Tunable to the upper part of FM broadcast band. Circuit requires the ability to tweak RF circuits by stretching or compressing coils. With mike and 9V battery clip. Operates from 6-12VDC. 2.75" x 0.625" x 0.5". Sold for educational purposes only.

Cellular Security Group 4 Gerring Rd., Gloucester, MA 01930. Some of the most sensitive and directional antennas for 800 (cellular bands) and 49 MHz "electronic baby-sitters".

# HEAR CORDLESS PHONES & BABY MONITORS
## High Performance Antennas for 46 to 49 MHz

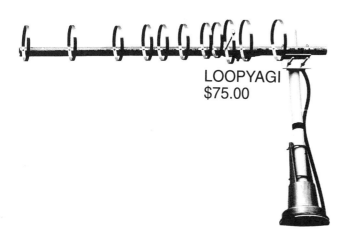

LOOPYAGI
$75.00

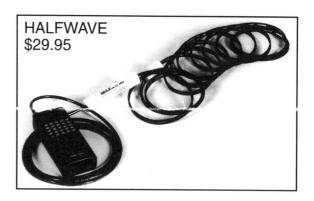

HALFWAVE
$29.95

## Dialed Number Recorder - DNR

The Racom MODEL 281D (DNR) can simultaneously monitor, locally or remotely, all activity on up to six target lines. For each interception call, the 281D will display and print a detailed call activity record for each telephone line monitored.

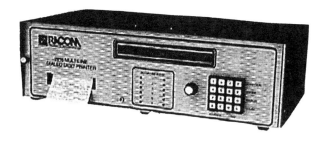

❏ Six independent telephone line monitoring capability
❏ Internal printer creates a hardcopy indicating all line activity including: date, time, duration & number dialed
❏ Separate minimized audio & cassette control outputs per line
❏ Front panel headset jack with volume control
❏ Programable target number alarms auto-activated unit
❏ Options include: Caller ID, Call Progress, Call Buffer, RS232 output & internal dialer per line for dial-up slaves

# WIRELESS VIDEO SYSTEM

- VTX2400 2.4 GHz Transmitter with omni antenna
- VRX2400 2.4 GHZ Receiver with omni antenna
- operators manual

All system functions controlled by a microcontroller which handles all interface with the user and saves system settings to EEPROM

**Surveillance Solutions** POB 91711 Mobile, AL 36691. www.dibbs.net/survsol
Covert video and audio specialists. OPS, but a good selection including Sony Z Box recorders, Watec cameras, video transmitters.

Some things we show where to buy direct, but some "dealers only" lines (such as Canon) also.

Good reputation. No printed catalog.

**Racom Products Inc.**, 5504 State Rd., Cleveland, OH 44134. www.racominc.com. Long manufacturer of "slave" phone taps and dialed number recorders. In the past non-voice capable units were sold to non-law enforcement to act as dialed number recorders.

In some cases the voice logging feature could be enabled after the issuance of a warrant. I believe they might be LE only at this point.

# Introducing microEar, the world's smallest radio receiver – fits entirely inside your ear.

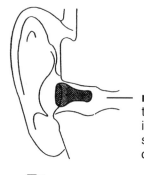

ACTUAL SIZE

It receives any portable radio transmission on a frequency you select within the FM frequency band FM-NB of 130 to 240MHz. The range depends on your transmitter's output, but you can anticipate a range of several hundred yards. Battery life —15 to 30 hours.

**microCom Induction Earphone** — the smallest induction receiver in the world - has a new automatic squelch circuit to alleviate the buzz caused by magnetic interference.

## Covert audio harness Collarset II

The Collarset II kit consists of a flat, combination microphone/inductor which is velcroed or pinned to your vest just over your collarbone. The inductor transmits an induction signal to the microCom receiver in the user's ear. The microphone is the lavaliere type of microphone which transmits the user's voice as well as the voice of anyone talking directly to the user. No need to talk into the mic — just talk. The press to talk switch can be located in the user's hand, belt or pocket. The price of **$799** includes the Collarset harness terminated for any radio and the microCom induction earphone.

**NOTE:** Alternative versions of Collarset II can be supplied with body press to talk switches and socket for consumer type headphones.

**Collarset II mic and inductor assembly** is concealed under your shirt. It is pinned or velcroed over user's collarbone.

**Press to talk switch** located in user's hand or pocket.

**Radio**

**Phonak Communications Murten Switzerland and Television Equipment Associates**POB 499 South Salem, NY 10590. A synergistic combination of a brand new Swiss product and a standard US offering, both sold by TEA.

The Collarset and microCom earphone are made by TEA. To utilize this system one conceals a receiver and a wire loop, or inductor, under one's clothing. The earpiece is positioned inside the ear where it will reproduce any audio picked up by the hidden receiver.

This system, although a bit bulky, it works well and eliminates those cute little "secret service" earphone wires.

The Phonak unit is the world's first in-ear receiver. That's right, the entire radio fits *inside* the user's ear where it will pass along any selected FM signal within the 130-240 MHz band.

The tiny unit includes a noise filter, narrow band capability, automatice frequency control, a squelch circuit and adjustable volume control.

TEA will provide a free 10 day test period to cops, governments and other serious buyers.

**Puretone Ltd.,** 10 Henley Business Park, Trident Close, Medway City Estate, Rochester, Kent ME2 4ER England. Some consultant is going to make a fortune teaching the British how to simplify their postal address system. At any rate PT offers a covert induction based audio system with a range of receivers from behind the ear, hearing-aid type receivers to sub-miniature custom built in-the-ear-canal plugs.

*R6-2*

Wired Earpiece
**£20.00**

*IR6*
Straight Shell with Integral On/Off Switch
Battery Type: 10A
**£75.00**

*IR7*
Straight Shell with Volume Control and On/Off Switch
Battery Type: 10A
**£96.00**

*T1*
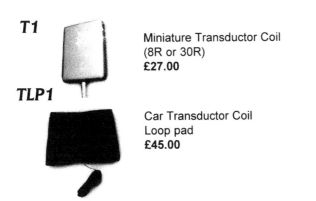
Miniature Transductor Coil (8R or 30R)
**£27.00**

*IR8*
Straight Shell
Battery Type: 312
**£69.00**

*TLP1*
Car Transductor Coil Loop pad
**£45.00**

*IR50*
Sub Miniature Earpiece
Battery Type: 5A
Class D Hi-Fidelity Sound
**£120.00**

*CIR*
Custom Built Earpiece for a perfect Anatomical Match & Secrecy
Battery Type 10A/5A
**£225.00**

**Sonic Solutions** 101 Rowland Way, Novato, CA 94945 www.sonic.com. A Mac based system of virtual filters and signal processing algorithms that can clean up either a pre-recorded or live sound by enhancing the energy in the vocal bands as well as notching out unwanted background audio.

The is a great system and has been used on every thing from the infamous O.J. telephone calls to DVD movie disks.

SS can take care of phase, distortions, echoes and background noise from any audio source.

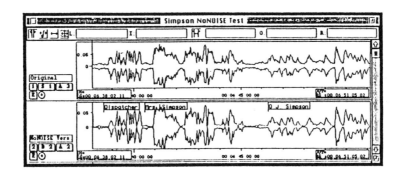

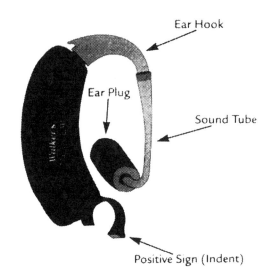

Ear Hook

Ear Plug

Sound Tube

Positive Sign (Indent)

**TACT'I EAR Walker's Game Ear, Inc.,** POB 1069 Media, PA 19063. Here's a new product that may be the most unusual piece of ES gear I've ever tested, much less recommended.

A simple question that a number of people have toyed with over the years – how does one actually conduct real time, nearby audio surveillance?

That is to say, suppose one desperately needs to overhear a quiet conversation in the vicinity, or the click of a gun hammer being cocked, or quiet footsteps on asphalt or the love moans of an 8 point white tail.

A new unit seems to fit this description pretty well. The **TACT'I EAR** is, well let's be honest, basically a tiny, tiny hearing aid.

Note our graphic is much larger than the actual unit.

The TE fits *behind* either ear where it nestles quite out of sight, thank you. A small clear plastic tube climbs over the top of the ear and culminates in an in-ear, one-size-fits-all foam ear plug.

What does the TE do? First and foremost it amplifies all sound reaching it by 6-8 times. Secondly it will automatically cut off all incoming sound when faced with a very loud noise.

Such as a gunshot...

The unit is advertised for use in both hunting as well as tactical situations where it might be very, very, important to hear a slight metallic "click" or nearby whisper.

Used correctly the TE really gives one an edge in quiet, or at least moderate noise environments. One can hear light footsteps in a quiet area or muted conversations from those not talking directly to you.

Under $200, a nice idea, well executed.

# PROFESSIONAL
## VHF/UHF CRYSTAL-CONTROLLED, AUTOMATIC
# TELEPHONE LINE TRANSMITTER.

**TRANSMITS ALL IN/OUT CALLS OF THE LINE.**
**RECEPTION:ANY VHF/UHF SCANNER.**

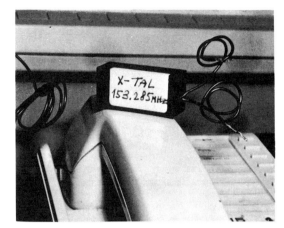

* **X-TAL CONTROLLED FREQUENCY.**
* **STATE -OF -THE -ART SMD** TECHNOLOGY.
* **MINIATURE SIZE** - FOR DISCREET & EASY INSTALLATION.
* **FULLY AUTOMATIC** - ACTIVATED UPON LIFTING OF RECEIVER.
* **POWERFUL RF OUTPUT** - RANGE: UP TO HALF A MILE.

**Special Electronic Security Products LtD.**, 12B Rahavat-Ilan St., Givat-Shmuel 54056 Israel www.sesp.co.il/~tunik. OEM supplier of covert audio equipment plus some other folks countermeasures gear.

Prices are good, some models operate above commercial FM (receivers are offered or one can use a scanner), at least one unit is crystal controlled and is available in either VHF or UHF up to 500 MHz.

**Shomer-Tec** Box 28070
Bellingham, WA 98228.

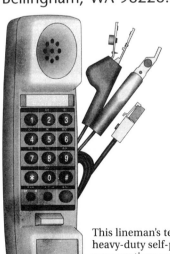

# LINEMAN'S TELEPHONE

This lineman's telephone lets you connect to a telephone line anywhere you have access to the wires! Just connect its special heavy-duty self-piercing alligator test clips to the red and green wires of a telephone line and you're set. You can then monitor conversations on that line as well as dial outgoing calls. Tone/pulse switchable dialing for compatibility with all telephone systems. Also comes with an RJ-11 (modular) connector cord. Last number re-dial and built-in ringer. WARNING: to be used only in a legal and lawful manner in full accordance with all applicable laws and F.C.C. regulations.

LMT ................................................................Lineman's Telephone ................................................

# R144 VHF FM Receiver

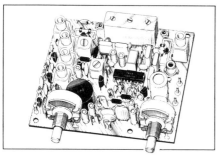

The R144 is a **premium-quality** two-meter receiver similar to the R100 except that it has a helical resonator in the front end after the first amplifier. As such, it has **excellent rejection of out-of-band signals**; so it is a good choice in applications where there are strong interfering signals to filter out. However, since the helical resonator has a limited tuning range, kits are only available for the 143-150 MHz band.

**PRICES:**

R144 Receiver kit for 143-150 MHz............................$169.00
   (Sorry, kits not avail. for com'l band.)
R144 Receiver wired/tested for 143-174 MHz...........$239.00
Crystal, commercial-grade ...........................................$12.00
A28 Coil Alignment Tool, required, see page 39...............$2.50
A2 Capacitor Alignment Tool, see page 39....................$2.50

**Hamtronics, Inc.,** 65 Moul Rd., Hilton, NY 14468. Intended for ham oriented hobbyists a number of products can be utilized for surveillance, TSCM and just listening.

Very, very, low prices.

**Grove Enterprises** POB 98, Brasstown, NC 28902 www.grove.net. General supplier of OPS including ICOM receivers, Bearcat scanners, Sony radios plus computer tuning software, decoders, preamps and antennas.

Around for many years, very respected, check their prices before ordering elsewhere.

# UNIDEN BC230XLT HANDHELD

## *Here's the update of the revered BC220XLT*

Uniden now includes a spare battery and charger with their popular hand-held scanner. Frequency coverage 29-54, 108-174, 406-512, and 806-956 MHz (less cellular). 200 memory channels in 10 banks include 10 priority channels for instant access to important transmissions regardless of monitoring status. TurboScan and TurboSearch provide 100 channel per second scanning and 300 channel per second searching! Preprogrammed service search affords single-key access to police, fire, emergency, aircraft, marine and weather frequencies! Data skip avoids noisy data transmissions, stopping only on valid communications! See pp. 8-9 for detailed specifications.

ORDER SCN24      SHIPPING
**$239⁹⁵**         $8 UPS
                 $10 US Mail
                 $14 Canadian UPS
                 $12.50 Canadian APP

*Comes with its own battery charger and spare battery.*

**ACCESSORIES**
BAT 8    BP 120 battery pack           $19.95
CAS 9    Professional Leather case     $19.95
DCC 7    Universal DC adapter          $15.95

# SP-200B Sound Enhancer

ORDER SPK 13
**$199⁹⁵**
Plus $8 UPS Shipping

*Guaranteed to improve audio quality on any receiver, scanner or transceiver!*

Grove's new and improved **SP-200B Sound Enhancer** (shown with the ICOM R8500) is really six products in one.

Why pay over $400 for separate audio components for your listening post—such as a speaker, adjustable notch/peak filter, audio amplifier, bass and treble equalizers, audio squelch, recorder activator and noise limiter—when you can have them all in one attractively styled oak cabinet! This quality accessory is guaranteed to improve reception on any receiver, scanner or transceiver. Peak desired signals while reducing or even eliminating interference. Ideal for voice, music, CW or data. Equipped with stereo-mono headphone jack for privacy. Powered by 12VDC@800 mA. AC adapter not included (order PWR04, $14.95).

The cabinet is hand-crafted in the mountains of North Carolina. Textured metal front panel resists fingerprints.

# The Covert 4

*They won't know it's there until you apprehend them.*

The Schell Covert 4 Signaling Transmitter features credit card dimensions for covert use in suitcases, envelopes and wallets. It is capable of being secreted to the extent of being virtually undetectable.

The Covert 4 is undetectable because it is passive until activated. It utilizes a two phase signal which can be rigged to give an officer a first and second alert capability. For example: A briefcase can be wired to signal you that it has been removed from its resting place. A second signal can tell you that the case has been opened or a money wrapper inside has been broken. The covert 4 is also useful as a panic button without alerting those nearby.

**Schell Electronics, Inc.,** 120 N Lincoln, Chanute, KS 66720. Respected supplier of credit card sized transmitters that are activated by trip wires, switches, motion detectors, and now a new product that will find transmitters in a building and/or function as a gate, doorway, driveway remote alert system.

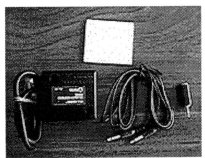

FOR YOUR CAR
CRX-20 CELLULAR RECORDER CONTROL

**BRD Security Products** 1926 S. Pacific Coast Highway, Suite 101, Redondo Beach, CA 90277 www.spybase.com. Reseller, but one that has put some time and effort into their choices. Nice hardwired audio room system, lapel mics, at least one wireless, Dan Gibson, a few Asian imports.

Prices not bad, Radio Shack +15%.

Another source worth looking at before you order basic surveillance gear.

# ROLL YOUR OWN

There is one viable alternative to purchasing electronic surveillance equipment – make your own.

The upside(s) include obtaining a $600 FBI quality unit for about $26 in parts as well as not worrying about the Feds, in one format or another, intercepting your mail and delivering it, ah, personally.

Note this does NOT make possession of devices "intended for surreptitious interception of conversation" any more legal. It's just, technically, at least with my third grade education, seems like the device is not really illegal until it's completed.

Now please don't take this to heart and tell the jury I told you it was okay, I'm sure we'd have a lot to talk about over the next 3-5 years but I have no real desire to change my particular living situation at this time.

A good rule to live by is if they want you, they will find a law ("conspiracy to commit") is one of my favorites , in order to come get you.

Downside(s) to the whip-it-together-yourself concept is that these are *not* kits – one must know electronic theory and hands-on construction/testing/alignment to even hope to get a working prototype.

Other option is you take plans and parts to the local Radio Shack (or better yet, a small electronics construction company (many such advertised in *Nuts And Volts*) and paysome kid to construct the unit.

I can provide three good, true and tested suppliers of construction plans for fairly cutting edge taps, bugs and assorted interesting devices.

First of all would be **Sheffield Electronics Co**. POB 377940 Chicago, IL 60637. SE offers a book, authored by its owner/operator, Winston Arrington, entitled **Now Hear This – Electronic Eavesdropping Equipment Design**.

This 126 page book consists strictly of schematics and construction details for equipment Mr. Arrington designed and used to sell; first to People On The Right Side Of The Law, and then to anyone who wanted them.

Until a friendly Fed pointed out the laws prohibiting such free enterprise.

Winston then put his designs in a book, which has been revised fairly recently.

I have built (hypothetically speaking, of course) a couple of his goods and they work as advertised.

Which is to say, well...

The designs are dated, most designed in the late 70's, early 80's and consist almost exclusively of discrete components. However the selection is quite complete and includes some pretty sophisticated gear such as a sub-zero carrier transmitter, various series and parallel telephone taps and, of course, the ubiquitous tampon transmitter.

Although an important scientific contribution, latter is probably not applicable to everybody...

Second selection would be **Spook Book II** by one Mick Tyner, available from Paladin Press. A good follow-up to Spook Book, this more generalized project includes many good schematics as well as background and descriptions of numerous eavesdropping devices.

Mr. Tyner is not, nor apparently has ever been actually in the spy biz, in fact has a rather interesting, non-allied career, but his material is quite good.

Third are individual plans from a gentleman named John Wilson. Mr. W. has designed and produced toys for a number of federal, state and local LE agencies and, like Mr. Arrington, used to sell his gear on the open market until the window of opportunity began to close.

John then began marketing his plans on a per-unit basis. A bit more pricey than buying a book, his construction details are more complete in nature.

The last time I spoke to John he was debating whether to continue selling his plans. If you are interested please contact him via email at Bugmanusal@aol.com.

It would be remiss of me not to point out that it is technically illegal to sell circuits for eavesdropping devices. This law was passed just after the Nixon/Watergate era and I'm not personally hip to anyone that has been busted for this nefarious crime, but if you have any interest in these collections it may be wise to not delay the purchase...

**Here is a list** of other potential surveillance sources – all of them have a web site and can be found by performing a key word search. Most, but not all, are resellers of OEM's covered elsewhere.

Advanced Digital Systems of St. Louis, Inc.
Advanced Electronics Group, Inc.
ATX Technologies, Inc.
Brandon Enterprises
Decatur Electronics, Inc.
DTC Communications
Eagle Eye Technologies, Inc
EarHugger Inc.
E.D.G. Enterprises
Electro-Optics
GSCI
H.E.S. Electronics
Hidden Camera Solutions
ID Control - in-car video systems
Intelpro co.
Intercept Investigations & Spy Technologies
Martel Electronics
MCH Communications
Mini Cameras. Com
MSE Inc.
Multicom
North American Investigations
Police Video Systems, Inc.
Protex, Inc.
Pure Optical Sound Technologies
PVP Communications, Inc.
Relco Sales Company, Inc.
Reliant Safety and Security
SecureTech Systems, Inc.
Security Plus Distributors
Shryock Communications
Sierra Pacific Innovations
Skaggs Telecommunications Service
SpectraTek Corporation
Spies Like Us
Spy Store, Inc
Spy Tech Agency D/B/A Probe, Inc.
Stridsberg Engineering, Inc.
Surveillance Solutions
SystemWare
Tac-Com Communications
Thermal-Vision, Inc.
Total Security Co.
Video Systems Plus

# COUNTER MEASURES

**Information Security Associates** 350 Fairfield Ave., Stamford, CT 06902. ISA has produced some of the finest full spectrum countermeasure receivers in the biz, recently they have combined their best receiver with a Windows software package to allow a more user friendly approach to rf detection.

The SmartScan system is both a software and hardware interface running from a notebook computer to ISA's ECR-2 countermeasures receiver.

Actually the ECR-2 is closer to a spectrum analyzer than a receiver, which is good news.

SmartScan allows the user to look at, demodulate and listen to every FM, AM, or video signal within range of the system. It will also compare a stored log of signals to a new sweep pinpointing any new entries into the local spectrum, analyze all signals for a specific sound source in the area (and silently alert the operator) as well as work with threshold alerts.

Besides this particular product ISA carries one of the widest/best lines of anti-eavesdropping gear in the country.

# Countermeasures Equipment and Services

### Boomerang[4] Non-Linear Junction Detector

The Boomerang[4] Non-Linear Junction Detector detects radio transmitters, amplified microphones, infrared and ultrasonic transmitters, tape recorders and other covert eavesdropping devices hidden in walls, ceilings, chairs, bookcases, plants, conference tables, etc.--EVEN WHEN THEY ARE NOT WORKING.

In operation the antenna is skimmed over the surface being examined. No physical contact is required. Most electronic circuits can be detected for several feet, even through dense materials, like concrete.

The Boomerang[4] is simple to use and extremely accurate. New design technology virtually eliminates false alarms by using dual frequency detection, enabling the user to tell the difference between a covert listening device and naturally occurring nonlinear junctions, simply by viewing the two antenna mounted LED bargraph meters.

Used by governments and industry worldwide.

### ECR-2 Countermeasures Receiver

The ECR-2 is a Spectrum Analyzer based receiver used to detect clandestine radio frequency transmitters in use worldwide. It tunes from 10 kiloHertz to 1000 Megahertz (the upper range is extendible to 7000 MHz, with optional range extenders). The ECR-2's high sensitivity assures detection of low powered transmitters, even in strong signal areas found in major metropolitan areas. High sensitivity also means that an area of 30 to 40 thousand square feet can be covered in just one sweep, making it extremely accurate and efficient.

The ECR-2 comes with a built-in printer for hard copy records and SRAM digital memory for electronic storage of detected signals. Video output aids in the analysis of television transmissions. The ECR-2 is supplied with all accessories needed to do a thorough sweep, including detailed manual, sound sources, antennas and powerline adapter for detecting transmitters on AC powerlines.

## *Super*Broom NLJD

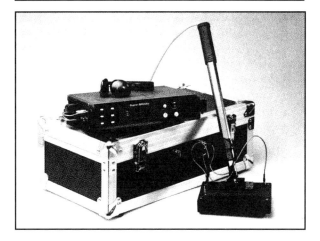

SuperBroom is an advanced non linear junction detector (NLJD) that uses the harmonic radar principle to sweep for bugging devices and other concealed electronics. SuperBroom will detect active, dormant and non-operational devices. During a sweep the antenna head is passed over the search area. Contained within the antenna head are three antennas. One antenna transmits the spectrally pure fundamental microwave signal that will cause electronic devices to re-radiate a harmonic series of return signals. The other two antennas receive the signals from the second and third harmonic returns of the fundamental transmission. By comparing the second and third harmonic returns SuperBroom's unique analysis techniques gives clear discrimination between electronic and non-electronic targets.

**Universal Radio, Inc.,** 6830 Americana Pkwy., Reynoldsburg, OH 43068 www.universal-radio.com. One stop shopping for receivers from Japan Radio, Grundig, Drake, GE, Sony, Sangean etc.

Universal also makes a couple of products such as the M-450 Universal Reader. Good prices, good selection.

**Audiotel International Ltd.,** Corby Road, Weldon, Corby NN17 3AR UK. OEM of the best known, and some of the best, counter surveillance systems in existence.

Inventors of the Scanlock nearfield receivers, used by virtually every intelligence agency in the world for eavesdropping detection/protection they have upgraded significantly with the addition of spectral analysis and computer interfacing.

Also have refined their Broom line of non-linear junction detectors as to allow for more reliable electronic device locating.

**UNIVERSAL
M-450
READER**

The self-contained Universal M-450 reader decodes many shortwave non-voice modes including: **Baudot, SITOR, FEC-A ASCII, SWED-ARQ, Weather FAX** (to the printer port). The scanner enthusiast can monitor the **ACARS** aviation teletype, plus **GOLAY** and **POCSAG** (512/1200/2400) digital pager modes. Even off-the-air decoding of **DTMF, CTCSS** and DCS. Big two-line, 20 character LCD and parallel printer port. The M-450 runs from 12 VDC or with the supplied AC adapter. No computer or monitor is required, however a serial port and computer control program are provided.
**Universal M-450**   List $449.95   Order #0450   **$399.95** (+$8)

**Bendix/King** 7505 Technology Dr., West Melbourne, Fl 32904. OEM of handheld and mobile transceivers. Some models use spread spectrum transmission, some will accept optional scrambling.

**Research Electronics Incorporated** 515 S. Old Kentucky, Rd., Cookeville, TN 38501 www.multipro.com/research/. Founded by an engineer who designed tricky things for the feds (and for AID, the major government surveillance supplier), REI has put together what is most likely the ultimate anti-electronic surveillance system ever offered.

The Omni Spectral Correlator (affectionately known as OSCOR) is a combination wideband receiver, spectrum analyzer and computer. OSCOR can be used in a manual mode to step through and identify every rf signal within reach (AM, FM, Video, IR, subcarriers, etc.) much like a super spectrum analyzer or thrown into a computer controlled mode which automatically highlights and identifies suspicious signals.

OSCOR uses several very hip detection techniques including taking an audio "fingerprint" of room-in-question audio and comparing it to every signal available for non-invasive transmitter locating.

Software controlled for easy updating, not cheap (think 13K+), but is the hottest thing around.

Used it, like it.

*The patented OSCOR correlator provides signal classification by correlating the demodulated audio of a received signal to the ambient noises of an environment.*

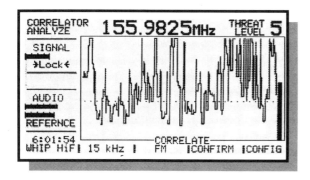

*The OSCOR analyzes each signal using patented sound pattern matching correlator.*

*The correlation process is integrated over time to ensure accurate correlation.*

*Based on the integrated correlation, the threat level of the signal is established. (scale from 1 to 5)*

*The signal shown in the figure is un-mistakenly an eavesdropping device.*

*For signals that are readily demodulated, the OSCOR easily classifies threatening signals. Signals that are not readily demodulated are automatically flagged for manual inspection.*

**Quark** 537 3rd Ave., New York, NY 10016. Expensive TSCM gear, mostly OPS including the OSCOR, Avcom spectrum analyzers.

**Martin Kaiser, Inc.,** POB 171 Cockeysville, MD 21030. Mr. Kaiser is somewhat infamous in both surveillance and counters thereof – in fact he designed and sold many interesting units to the feds until a rather strange incident wherein he was arrested for possessing his own devices, while at a sales meeting with the FBI (this is true, you might want to take note of this:).

Since then he has shifted his emphasis to countermeasures and bomb detection devices. He's a wiz of an engineer and his stuff is top notch, not really duplicated per se anywhere else.

Resold in many OTP's catalogs for more.

Money, that is.

Full countermeasure kits, telephone analyzers, nearfield detectors that actually work, feedback detectors, line tracers and so on and so forth.

Mr. Kaiser recently served as a technical advisor to the movie Enemy Of The State and I can tell you from personal experience that his equipment is so good it is feared (as well as used) by many law enforcement agencies...

**2045B**                               **FEEDBACK DETECTOR**

This unit covers the radio spectrum from 100KHz to over 1000MHz and detects many battery or AC and telephone line powered radio frequency (RF) and infrared (IR) optical transmitters by using the "feedback" technique. That's where the suspect transmitter hears the noise from the loudspeaker of the 2045B and the 2045B, in turn, detects what the transmitter hears, thereby causing a feedback squeal. Despite its simplicity, this detector offers a high degree of effectiveness and reliability. The system is supplied with the amplifier/speaker, probe assembly, RF antenna, AC input cable, optical (IR) probe, headset, intructions and carrying case. The amplifier is powered by 6 "AA" batteries while the optical probe contains a single "AA" battery (Alkaline always preferred).

**2055HA**                  **"NEARFIELD" RF DETECTOR**

This differential antenna/detector covers from 10 to over 1,000MHz and solves many of the problems encountered in very high level signal locations such as metropolitan areas. The level of radio frequency (RF) radiation from computers and other electronic equipment can also be observed with this unit. Supplied with amplifier/indicator assembly, RF head, two antennas, head extension rods and cables, special 2,000 ohm headset and carrying case. Uses two 9-volt batteries and incorporates internal battery test circuits.

**OptoElectronics** 5821 NE 14th Ave., Ft. Lauderdale, FL 33334 www.optoelectronics.com. Primarily receivers and frequency counters for countermeasures and communications (see entries in both sections), some of Opto's products are surveillance oriented.

## Micro DTMF Decoder

The Micro DTMF Decoder housed in a pager style case is ideal for portable hands free operation. With its built-in microphone, DTMF tones can be decoded from tape recorders, receivers, two-way radios, etc... Tones are displayed on the Micro Decoders 12 digit LCD display and automatically stored in the 2000 character non-volatile memory for review. A 3.5mm audio input located on the side of the Micro Counter can also be used for direct connection to a receivers audio.

## FEATURES
- Pager Style Case w/ beltclip
- Internal Microphone for radio speaker or tape recorder pickup
- Line audio input jack for direct

# High Speed, Nearfield Receiver

**Capri Electronics** 1238 Hwy., 160-B POB 589 Bayfield, CO 81122. For 21 years Capri has been making some of best low end counter surveillance gear available. Their line is a staple for many dealers.

At one point they stopped selling retail – this policy has been revised and one can now buy at retail (still much less than thru most resellers) in single quantities or at full discount if one springs for 10 products.

Transmitter detectors, line drivers, IR finders and the scan record.

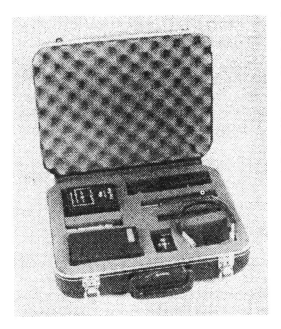

The CMS-11 Countermeasures Set is designed for the person who wants to be able to perform the basic countermeasures checks either for his own security or as a business offering the service to others. The set is built around the TD-53 Advanced Transmitter Detector and consists of the following items:

Torfino Enterprises, Inc., 3500 Fairland Farms Rd., Suite 3, West Palm Beach, FL 33414 www.torfino.com. OEM of handheld rf detectors, metal and weapons detectors.

## RADIO FREQUENCY *NEAR-FIELD TRANSMISSION DETECTOR

### FEATURES

- Freq. range 5Mhz-1.5Ghz
- Dual operating modes
- Effective *Near-field alert while worn by an individual
- Adjustable ambient Radio Frequency level
- Monitor/Quick-sweep capability with earphone
- Two detachable antennas
- High brightness dual color LED (Light Emitting Diode) indicators
- Precision fit cold rolled steel case with scratch resistant black painted finish
- 1 year limited warranty

Jarvis International Intelligence, Inc., 11720 East 21st St., Tulsa, OK 74129. TSCM sweeps, great counter/surveillance and entry courses and several pieces of excellent TSCM gear including a sweep receiver, time domain reflectometer and line tracers/amplifiers.

## JII

## FEEDBACK

## DETECTOR

**Datong Electronics Ltd.,** Clayton Wood Close, West Park, Leeds England LS16 6QE. Very slick, high end dedicated countermeasures receivers and direction finding equipment.

Been around a long time, good reputation, good stuff.

**Great Southern Security** 513 Bankhead Ave., Carroliton, GA 30117. Line of inexpensive bug and tap finders, white noise generators, body wire detectors, etc.

**SecurityCall, Inc.,** POB 33194 Los Gatos, CA 95031. Patented "telephone wiretap detector alarm system". The SC is a unique unit consisting of a small proprietary computer ("master unit") and a number of slaves this system operates in a fashion unlike anything else on the market.

Basically the SC can be trained to look at any building phone system, memorize a series of electronic measurements (voltage, impedance, draw, etc.) and then automatically compare the stored readings with new input from entire wiring set up in order to see if any changes have taken place.

If said changes have occurred the unit will beep-alarm the user.

This unit was not designed for TSCM work but rather for companies to set up a phone firewall and then be able prove to prove due diligence in protecting their clients information for electronic surveillance.

The idea is unique and it works *providing* the system is clean of any taps when the SC is installed and "trained".

If tap(s) exist at installation the SC will, of course, assume they belong in the works and consider their effects to be normal for any further testing.

If used correctly provides a unique layer of security.

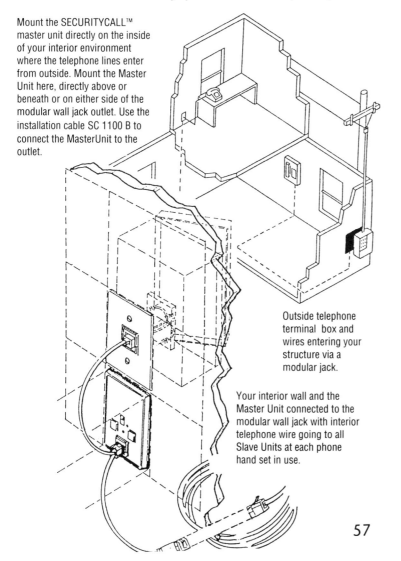

Mount the SECURITYCALL™ master unit directly on the inside of your interior environment where the telephone lines enter from outside. Mount the Master Unit here, directly above or beneath or on either side of the modular wall jack outlet. Use the installation cable SC 1100 B to connect the MasterUnit to the outlet.

Outside telephone terminal box and wires entering your structure via a modular jack.

Your interior wall and the Master Unit connected to the modular wall jack with interior telephone wire going to all Slave Units at each phone hand set in use.

Many items not designed for TSCM work will function with some degree of effectiveness during sweeps. Jensen Tools (see General Suppliers), Radio Shack as well as a number of telephone equipment houses offer lineman's handsets, line tracers, squealers, receivers etc., at non-inflated prices and should be considered as possible inclusions.

# PSA-35A Portable Spectrum Analyzer

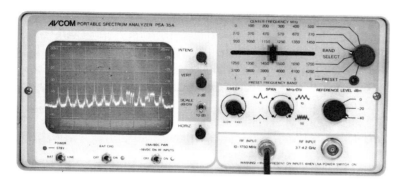

**Avcom** 500 Southlake Blvd., Richmond, VA 23236 www.avcompfva.com. OEM of spectrum analyzers, microwave and satellite receivers Avcom is not designed primarily for counter surveillance tasks but their equipment is first rate, works for TSCM and is thousands of dollars cheaper than, say, Tektronix…

**FEATURES:**

* Frequency Coverage 10-1750 MHz 3.7-4.2 GHz
* Basic enough to begin with - sophisticated enough to grow with. Ku and C band compatible.
* Lightweight, portable, battery operated - ideal for field test situations.
* Accurately measures wideband signals commonly used in the satellite communications industry.
* Built-in DC Block and Power for LNA's and LNB's.

Trouble-shoot system problems by observing output signals from LNA's, BDC's, Line Amplifiers and Splitters, and other RF signals components. Measure block system signal balance.

Identify and resolve terrestrial interference problems quickly and precisely by displaying offending signals on the PSA-35A. Customers can be shown the nature of TI problems for clearer understanding.

Measure and document satellite communication system performance after installation or service. Customer should be given a copy of results per AVCOM's SASAR (Spectrum Analyzer System Analysis Report) to insure customer confidence and satisfaction.

Progressive Satellite Communication Dealers, Repair Centers, and Manufacturers will find AVCOM's PSA-35A Spectrum Analyzer to be an indispensable instrument for rapid testing and alignment of satellite equipment. Problems that might otherwise take hours, even days to resolve, can be identified and corrected in minutes, saving time and money, while reinforcing customer good will. An AVCOM Spectrum Analyzer will pay for itself quickly.

**Allison Technology Corporation** 8343 Carvel, Houston, TX 77036 www.atcweb.com. Inexpensive "virtual" test gear that combines hardware modules, controlling software and a computer to create oscilloscopes, spectrum analyzers, voltmeters.

**The O-SCOPE Ie** includes all of the advantages of the Ip plus a versatile external trigger and dual channel capability. A second O-Scope module and software are required for the dual trace function.

O-Scopes offer several features not found in conventional analog oscilloscopes. First, they are small and lightweight; can be carried in tookit or briefcase. Second, trace sweeps can be stored on the display loaded into other programs. Fourth, the spectrum analyzer mode provides a graphic display of the frequencies of the incoming signal. Fifth, captured sweeps can be output to a printer. Sixth, numerical values for frequency, period and voltages (DC, RMS, MIN, MAX, and PEAK to PEAK) are continuously displayed.

**BEMA Inc.,** POB 176 Dumfries, VA 22026. Neat stuff! OEM of portable, lightweight rf shielded enclosures, "designed to provide quick access and optimum portability to protect proprietary information within computer and communications environments".

Okay...

Think of tents made from Mylar – okay that's a major over simplification, but BEMA's portable "rooms" enclosing specific pieces of gear or entire areas will effectively prevent almost all types of electromagnetic eavesdropping including Tempest computer violations.

**CCS** 360 Madison Ave., New York, NY 10017 www.spyzone.com. Very expensive countermeasures gear plus anti-bark dog collars, stash stones, plant safes, computer transmission systems etc.

Remember that almost every supplier who carries any sort of surveillance gear also stocks some sort of countermeasures equipment. See we sell you the bug and then we sell you...

Point being one may wish to check the surveillance section as well as spy shops and general suppliers before ordering that one in a life time, dream TSCM goodie.

# Secure Voice Communication

### SV2000 TELEPHONE AND DataENCRYPTOR

Business Security AB´s voice and data encryptor SV2000 provides secure voice and data communication in one integrated package. The voice quality is extremely good in encrypted mode. On the display you can read the name of your conversation partner. This provides additional security.

### KEY MANAGEMENT

SV2000 has a true hardware random generator. This generates a true random 256 bits key which will be stored on the personal smartcard and on the key distribution card. Tied to the encryption key on the personal card, you can store an ID (name) of the person or organization to whom the actual encryption key will be used for.

**Business Security** Greenhouse, Box 110 65, S-220 11 Lund, Sweden. Over the past decade the US government has attempted both to limit the exportation of usable encryption as well as limit the key code length on all encryption methods to a length where the Feds would have no problem reading the contents.

During this period the Swiss developed a couple of outstanding encryption algorithms, in particular one known as SBLH.

BS's phone, fax and data scrambling units use a 128 bit version of SBLH. This is, at least up until now, a completely unbreakable code. I mean the NSA doesn't want you to own these products...

Highly recommended company for high end encryption.

**Transcrypt International** 4800 Northwest 1st Street, Lincoln, NE 68521 www.transcrypt.com. Transcrypt can equip virtually any piece of communication gear with secure encryption. They offer a wide line of scramblers starting with simple inversion units (cheap, but not very secure), moving up to slow hopping inversion scramblers which provide medium level security to fast (750 million codes) hopping units which provide security against all but the most technically capable eavesdropping techniques.

Besides these analog scramblers Transcrypt also offer high level DES based digital encrypting units. The units are marketed as add-on modules for virtually every make and model of two way radio or they can modify existing units.

One can also purchase complete units including pre-scrambled Motorola cell phones, cellphone scramblers, landline encryption units, and even protected fax machines.

One of the best providers of secure communications available.

## DME-2 Series Landline Encryptor

Transcrypt's DME-2 provides both digital encryption and analog voice privacy for landline telephones. The DME-2 plugs between a single line analog telephone and the wall jack to supply a full complement of voice privacy solutions. Backwards compatibility allows the DME-2 to operate with Transcrypt's PX, CX, and LX voice privacy units. The DME's lighted display panel indicates the security status of each phone call to assure the user that communication is being coded.

## PX™ Series Cellular Scrambler

The PX cellular scrambler embeds in the Motorola MicroTAC™ cellular phone. The module, which adds virtually no weight or size to the phone, is activated when the user enters a code on the phone's keypad. An intermittent red LED indicator confirms that communication is secure.

## SEF Series Fax Encryptor

CryptoFax Models SEF 300 and SEF 400 are stand-alone fax security devices that bring an unprecedented level of protection and ease-of-use to any fax environment. With a single self-contained unit, users worldwide can ensure total message security, authenticate both sending and receiving parties and guarantee access to vital transmitted information solely by the intended recipient.

Nanny-cams and other low-powered video transmitters are frequently used for video surveillance. These video transmitters are disguised as VCRs, clocks, clock radios, pictures, desk accessories, and are even installed in stuffed teddy bears.

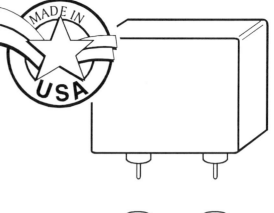

These hidden "eyes" can transmit images over distances varying from 100 to 500 feet.

Due to their low power and high operating frequencies, these video transmitters CANNOT be readily detected. In fact, NONE of the well-known "bug" detectors on the U.S. market (some costing as much as $4,800 to $11,500) can do the job! Some of them CLAIM to be able to detect these "nanny-cams" and other low-powered video transmitters, but they simply CANNOT. **The FD-3000 will detect these transmitters from 6 to 10 ft. away!**

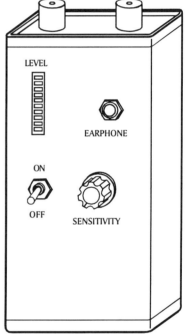

**Viking International** 150 Executive Park Blvd. #4600, San Francisco, CA 95134. OEM of some of the better, low cost TSCM gear in the US. Designed by an engineer who has, for the last 20 years, constantly produced very good products.

The FD-3000 video detector is one of the few (at any cost) units I've tried that will reliably detect 900 MHz and 2.4 GHz video transmitters.

**Intelligence Incorporated** 3555 S. El Camino Real, San Mateo, CA 94403 www.intelligence.to. No hardcopy catalog – several hard to find countermeasures units including the C3I telephone slave finder, the ATS, a tap stopper that actually defeats most forms of telephone tapping and the Comsec countermeasures receiver.

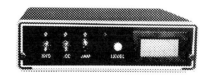

# VIDEO SURVEILLANCE

See page 119 for a system similar to the one in Karen's 34th Street house.

**VMI** (Visual Methods Incorporated) 35 Charles St., Westwood, NJ 07675 www.visualmethods.com. Long respected leader in covert video innovations. VMI has, over the last 10 or 15 years, designed and produced some of the best covert video apps around including the camera-in-a-sprinkler, complete pinhole drilling and mounting kits and much more.

The owner lectures at many professional conferences, just wrote a good book on this very subject.

| WCT804B-8 | B&W | 8mm | Battery |
|-----------|-----|------|---------|
| WCT804B-11 | B&W | 11mm | Battery |
| WCT804C-8 | Color | 8mm | Battery |
| WCT804C-11 | Color | 11mm | Battery |

**WCT806 Series**

Wireless
Smoke Detector
Camera (side view)

**WCT805 Series**

Wireless
"No Smoking" Sign
Camera

**WCT829 Series**

Wireless
Wall Clock
Camera

**WCT809 Series**

Wireless
Table Top Radio
Camera

**KT & Company, Ltd.**, 1006, Geukdong VIP bldg., 14-8, Yaido-Dong, youngdeugpo-ku, Seoul, Korea. To use their words, "micro vision, ultra mini vision, cylinder vision, professional CCTV  and board cameras.

OEM, something for everybody.

**Marshall Electronics** POB 2027 Culver City, CA 90231 www.mars-cam.com. Cameras, lenses, low cost fiber optic borescope, mini coax cable, gain antennas monitors, a complete line of covert and industrial video equipment at rock bottom prices that only compare with some Asian suppliers.

A single chip board camera for $50! Check these people out.

# World's Smallest "C" Mount Camera!
## *Ultra Low Light Sensitivity Allows Monitoring in Almost Total Darkness*

- 1½" square x 1" deep, 3 ounces
- 0.05 lux, HAD sensor technology
- 510 x 492 pixels
- 380 lines of resolution
- Automatic electronic iris
- 12 VDC, 100 mA, 1.2W

*CCD = charge-coupled Device*

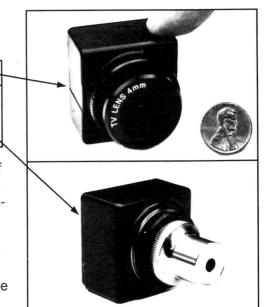

**V-1055**

**V-1055 with 25mm pin-hole lens**

This micro size, state-of-the-art camera is only an inch-and-a-half square, yet is a full function, low light CCD camera with 380 lines of resolution and a built-in "C/CS" mount. Because of a new high-tech sensor, this camera needs only 0.05 lux, which outperforms human sight in many low light conditions. At an inch-and-a-half square, it can fit almost anywhere. With the "C" mount, there is a whole series of miniature, standard, and microscope lenses to choose from, making this an excellent choice for low cost machine vision, robotics, and computer imaging applications.

# Miniature Coax Runs Video & Power On One Cable

- Up to 1000 ft video
- Dual video or video + power

*Instead of camera tubes, most modern video cameras now use light-sensitive integrated circuits (tiny electronic devices) called "charge-coupled devices" (CCDs).*

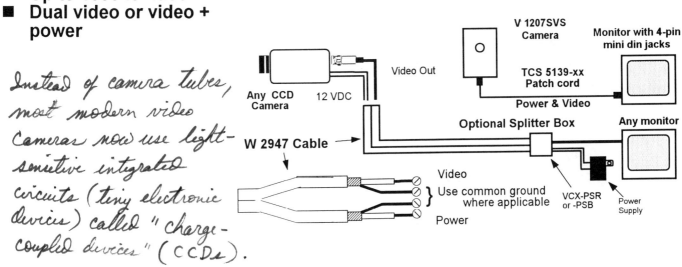

**Any CCD Camera**  **12 VDC**

**W 2947 Cable**

**Video Out**

**V 1207SVS Camera**

**TCS 5139-xx Patch cord**

**Power & Video**

**Monitor with 4-pin mini din jacks**

**Optional Splitter Box**

**Any monitor**

Video
} Use common ground where applicable
Power

**VCX-PSR or -PSB**

**Power Supply**

*For more info, Do a Find on "television" in Encarta*

# "Clock" Video Camera

No one will suspect that this operating quartz clock contains an undetectable black & white CCD camera The 5.5mm wide angle lens allows for totally "COVERT" operations. The .2 Lux allows this camera to view in low light *better than the human eye.* Its micro electronic sensors adjust for all light changes. The black and white board camera built inside this clock has high resolution of more than 400 lines. Power supply included. Dimensions approximately 10 ½"inches in diameter.

**SPY OUTLET** POB 337, Buffalo, NY 14226. Reseller, covert video, recorders, some infrared gear, time lapse recorders, lockpicks, a few books.

# PH200 Black/White Pinhole Board Camera

*The best Pinhole in the industry...*

**PH200 5.5mm Pinhole Chip Camera**

**Box Camera**

**Smoke Det'r Camera**

**Clock Camera**

**Exit Sign Camera**

**Speaker Camera**

**Elevator Camera**

**SpyTech** 2028 Yonge St., Toronto, CA M4S 1Z9. Another example of a left-over spy store. Minox cameras, JVC recorders, Dan Gibson Mics, Panasonic VCR's, mini board camera(s) the usual "hidden in a smoke detector-exit sign" covert stuff plus some Japanese products at very high markups.

**Eltec Instruments, Inc.**, Central Business Park, Datona Beach, FL 32120. Thermal, IR and laser detectors as well as some very interesting security products.

# Model 862
## IR-EYE™
## Long Range
## Passive Infrared
## Telescopes

**OSSI Optical Surveillance Systems.**, 13 E St., SW, Arrdmore, OK 73402. Very reasonably priced board cameras as well as complete car/body worn packages.

## *Surveillance*
# Video
# Camera

Tiny B/W video camera features *Changeable* lenses, Electronic Iris, CMOS design, .9 lux, and operates for *days* on a single 12V powerpack (or 6-18VDC). All this at a low price that's *almost* unbelievable!

*Shown with optional lens*

*Price Breakthrough!*

# $49⁹⁵

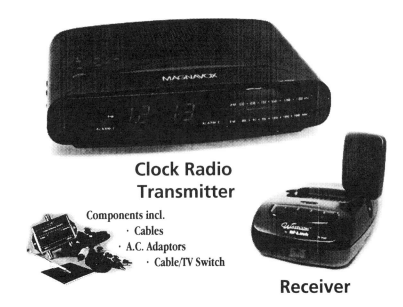

**Clock Radio Transmitter**

Components incl.
· Cables
· A.C. Adaptors
· Cable/TV Switch

**Receiver**

**Adler Video Systems** 711 W. Ivy St., Glendale, CA 91204. This is *the* big secret in the security/covert video business. AVS is primarily a distributor but they do sell singles of virtually every manufacturer one can visualize from Sony to Baraka.

Also left-over sales every couple of weeks on cameras, recorders, mounts, wireless, hidden and "normal" video monitors, recorders and ancillary equipment.

Adler is where the spy shops shop (or should, at any rate) and you can too.

Nice newsletter about the hottest products, deals.

Get on the mailing list.

**Counter Spy Shop of Mayfair London** 9557 Wilshire Blvd., Beverly Hills, CA 90212 www.spyzone.com. Despite the fancy title this is the Southern Cal version of CCS (Communication Control Systems – NY). Slick color catalog, board cameras, nanny cams, pinholes hidden in exit signs, car antennas, pens etc.

Mostly resellers. Very expensive.

**Sunkwang Electronics Ltd.**, 8-1, Wonmi-dong, Wonmi-ku, Buchon-shi, Kyunggie-do, Korea. Serious OEM of board and encased micro cameras. Prefer to deal in quantity, may sell singles, dealer prices on small quantities.

Find 'em in many, many "spy" catalogs at 2-6 times the original price:

## SPECIFICATION (SK-1010)

| MODEL NO. | SK1010E(EIA) | SK1010C(CCIR) |
|---|---|---|
| IMAGE SENSOR | 1/3″ CCD(B/W) | |
| EFFECTIVE PIXEL | 250,000 | 290,000 |
| SCANNING SYSTEM | 525 LINE INTERLACE | 625 LINE INTERLACE |
| OUTPUT SIGNAL | 1.0Vp–p / 75ohm SYNC. NEGATIVE POLARITY | |
| LIGHT SENSITIVITY | 0.1LUX(SCENE) | |
| RESOLUTION | HORI. : 360 TV–LINE | HORI. : 380 TV–LINE |
| LENS | FIXED FOCUS LENS, f=3.6mm, F=2.0, STANDARD | |
| IRIS | AUTO–IRIS CONTROLLED BY ELECTRONIC SYSTEM | |
| S/N RATIO | 45dB OR MORE(AGC OFF) | |
| GAMMA | 0.45 | |
| AGC | ON | |
| POWER SUPPLY | DC 9V–16V | |
| CONSUMED CURRENT | 150 mA MAX | |
| SHUTTER SPEED | 1/60 – 1/32,000 | 1/50 – 1/32,000 |
| TEMP. & HUMIDITY | –10℃ – + 50℃, RH 95% MAX. | |
| WEIGHT | 30g | |

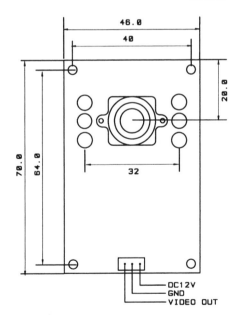

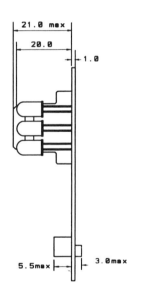

**IOU Keh Electronic Co.**, Ltd., 6F, No. 10 Lane 16, Sec. 2, Szu Chuan Rd., Pan Chyau, Taipei, Taiwan. Boards, ribbons, domes, monitors, splitters, housings, brackets, lenses, whew...

**Watec America Corporation** 3155 East Patrick Lane, Las Vegas, NV 89120 www.watec.com. Watec's are, with out a doubt some of the best micro/miniature board and enclosed surveillance cameras on the world market.

Sold in many catalogs, one would be wise to ask for the original catalog, pick the correct unit and then ask the nice Watec folks for a list of dealers.

Compare prices; buy.

# WAT-66OD-6O

1/4" B&W CCD Image Sensor
Number of Pixels: 280K Pixels
Resolution: 380 TV Lines
Minimum Illumination: 0.5 Lux @ $f1.2$
Auto Electronic Iris (1/60 -1/10,000 Sec)
Lens: 6mm Micro Lens
Operation Temperature: -10° ~ +40°C
Power Supply: 9V DC ± 10% (100mA)

**Camera Dimensions:**
29mm(W) x 29mm(H) x 23mm(L)  (1.16 x 1.16 x 0.93")

*Also available with 2.5mm, 3.8mm, 8mm, 25mm Micro Lens

**For use with the WAT-AD502A 9V DC power supply**

**Security Products International** 223D Stiger St., Hackettstown, NJ 07840. Distributor of a whole bunch of cameras, kits, systems, glasses, in-the-clock, Cannon, Sony, Panasonic, Chugai, Silent Witness – hell you get the idea.

Check the prices before buying elsewhere.

## Guardian Angel II

Plant camera w/wireless Tx
Wireless motion detector
VCR w/time & date stamp
Charger system
Easy setup

**90184-2 Guardian Angel II**                    **$1695.00**

**Operative Supply** POB 2343 Atlantic Beach, NC 28512. A catalog "spy shop"
OS stocks several video products from people like VMI, and even Knox.
Charge for the catalog.

## MICRO VIDEO CAMERAS

**OPERATIVE SUPPLY**

has the complete
WATEC line of black
and white and color
cameras. We also offer
Auto Focus Lens, Pow-
ers Supplies Accessories
and Wireless Police
Versions. Please call,
write or FAX us for
additional information

**Confidential Communications Ltd.** Unit F33-F35 Imex House, The Park
Business Center, Kilburn Park Rd., London NW6 5LF UK www.confidential-
communications.co.uk. Reseller and OEM of covert equipment. Over 200
products including covert surveillance cameras, transmitters, receivers and
computer based recording systems.

## 'Smallest Pinhole Camera in the World'

**Actual size**

**Misumi Electronics Corp.**, 5F-3, No. 70, Jiann-Liow Rd., Chung Ho City, Taipei Shann Taiwan R.O.C. www. misumi.com.tw. OKAY, okay the big secret in covert video – Where do the big resellers, upper end spy shops, some feds and smart people from all walks of life get their board and miniature cameras?

Misumi makes some of the best covert gear around including:
- pinholes,
- IR,
- encapsulated
- dome and sub-miniature dome

Misumi "prefers to sell in quantity" but they will sell single units. Prices? I just finished one catalog offering "the world's smallest video camera" for $149.00.

Misumi sells the unit, in single quantities, for *$25.00.*

**Inter-Kor Electronics Co., Ltd.**, 40-10, Wonmi-Dong, Wonmi-Ku, Bucheon City, Kyeongki-Do Korea. OEM 20 board, pinhole, C-mount units plus encased and dome cameras.

**Polaris Industries** 470 Armour Dr., NE, Atlanta, GA 30324. Manufacturer and reseller. Wide line of products, good to very good prices, full staff for technical support, same day shipping.

Check out Polaris before buying from a reseller.

# MB-1060C COLOR CAMERA WITH SVHS

## *MB-1060C High Resolution SVHS Digital Color Camera -$419.95*

- **480-Line horizontal resolution**
- **50dB signal-to-noise ratio**
- **Excellent color reproduction**
  For crisper natural image, digital RGB signal processing provides well-balanced color reproduction which is beyond the comparison with other micro cameras.
- **Auto Gain Control (AGC)**
- **Auto Light Control**
  Auto Light Control keeps contrast video signal level by controlling AGC function and ELC function automatically.
- **Auto Backlight Compensation**
  Auto backlight compensation equipped with a backlight compensation mode as part of the light control function. More photometric weight is given to the center of the screen than to the edges, where backlighting would most likely be located.

- **Versatile output signal: composite x 2, Y/C x 1**
  To avoid cross-color, MB-1060C features Y/C (S-Video)
  output which provides well-balanced colors.
- **Reliable signal-board-designed CCU**
- **C-Mount capability**

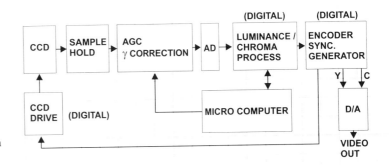

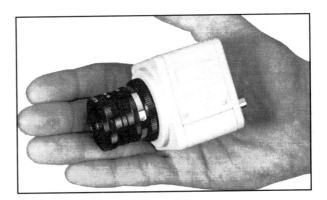

**Liteon** 9F, #233-2, Pao-Chiao Rd., Hsin-Tien, Tapei Hsien, Taiwan. Boards, ribbons, domes.

The Sony EVO 220 is the heart and soul of most covert video operations, coupled with its Z-Box Event Recorder the 220 can be programmed to turn on at specific signals, run for so long, turn off, as well as more tricks than my pet wolf knows.

The 220 has been strapped to more bodies than the cross-my-heart-bra for covert "sting" type operations from drug buys to bribing senators. Coupled with a hidden camera it does a fine job of recording most close-in nefarious transactions.

The system does have a few shortfalls – most pager/tie/sunglasses cameras run from their own power sources, the 220 from another, there's really no way to tell if the unit is actually recording, power sources run down at different intervals, etc.

**ISIS Investigations, Inc**. 427 S. Vine, Tyler TX 75702 www.isisinv.com. Is an investigative agency who has utilized the Sony system in a variety of different operations. They grew tired of the shortcomings and had their in-house engineer design a small interface box that works with modified 220's to solve many potential problems.

Their box converts the 220 battery voltage to allow operation of most mini cameras (pagers, etc.) from the 220's own power supply. The interface also includes an auto gain audio amplifier which improves the sound quality measurably as well as a lighted remote on/off switch that controls both the camera and the recorder.

Stash the 220 in a fanny pack, purse, strapped to your body, run the camera wires to the interface, put the control switch in a comfortable position and hit it...

Waiting for a dishonest waiter or drug dealer to come back from his contact? Turn the machine off with a touch of the switch, don't waste tape filming the environment. If you place the switch where you can see the red glow you always know when you are actually recording.

ISIS sells the entire package including a pager cam and modified 220 or will modify yours for a fee. They also offer a selection of board cameras, VCR's and

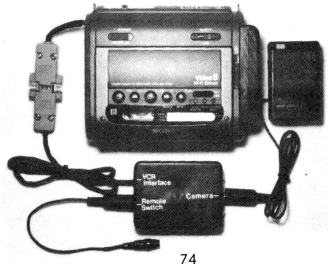

**ATV Research** 1301 Broadway, Box 620, Dakota City, NE 68731 www.atvresearch.com. Although most products are aimed somewhere between the security and civilian markets ATV has added some very inexpensive, interesting products to their catalog.

2.4 GHz wireless audio/video transmission systems at about the same price one can get from Asian OEM's. High performance antenna systems, mini wireless video module ($65!) board cams, and a very reasonably priced FCC approved video/audio system with a range of up to *3 miles!*

Get the catalog.

# Wireless Video MODULE

New lower cost over previous model

### Great for many covert and body-cam applications!

8-9vdc @ 135ma * 2.0" x 2.2" x 0.5" * Includes flat pad ant. * Typical Range: 100-500 feet, depending on obstacles back to the receiver.

**Important:** These modules require soldering to small terminals for power, video and audio leads and should not be purchased by those not skilled in working with such microelectronics. A moderate amount of knowledge about RF transmission characteristics is also helpful.

**CW3800** transmitter module with pad antenna... **$65!**
**CW7800RX** companion receiver with AC power supply...$79

as low as **$105** in qty

The WaveCom Jr. 2.4Ghz FM transmission system comes complete: transmitter, receiver, directional circular polarized antennas and power supplies. Ideal for satellite, VCR's, CCTV and covert jobs!

$259

### Model WC-WS040-100

Here's what you get: A Wavecom receiver specially equipped with a 10db gain circular polarized pad antenna. (Actually a stacked array). Typically can extend range out to 600-1000 feet.

**Mythos Multmedia Inc.**, 2629 Barrington Ct., Hayward, CA 94545. A couple of PC digital cameras, one dome, a four camera system as well as custom manufacturing and design for large customers.

**Mitsubishi Electronics America, Inc.**, 5665 Plaza Dr., Cypress, CA 90630 www.mitsubishi.com. Time lapse VCR's , printers, etc.

Not sold direct but will supply a list of dealers.

Other distributors of CCTV and security oriented video products are: **Ademco Distribution, Inc.**, 180 Michael Dr., Syossett, NY 11791, **Richardson Electronics, Ltd.**, 13105 Northwest Fwy., Suite 1090, Houston, TX 77040 and **Costar Video Systems** 40925 County Center Dr., Temecula, CA 92591.

*TA-24RT-DC*

**Team Crest** 3706 Alliance Dr., Greensboro, NC 27407 www.crestelctronics.com (note this is how the site is spelled in their catalog, might also want to try it with "electronics" spelled correctly).

**GBC (CCTV) Corp.** 280 Huyler St., S. Hackensack, NJ 07606. A very large supplier of both security and covert video equipment, GBC seems to offer a number of their own units as well as several Asian companies they deal with and/or do research with.

One of the most varied line of board cameras hidden in clocks, smoke detectors, telephones, mirrors, photos, speaker phones, thermostats, you name it – their products are picked up and sold by many other dealers.

One product, a PIR and camera in one housing seems to be an exceptionally nice idea, probably a bit more expensive than the direct Asian model mentioned elsewhere in this chapter, also features more features.

## Now Alarm Installers Don't Have To Compromise To Get A Quality CCTV Camera

- Electronics adapted from the highly proven Sentrol Sharpshooter™
- Sealed optics prevent false alarms
- Advanced 3D signal processing (speed, size, shape)
- Comes with standard wide angle lens - five additional lenses available as accessories
- High immunity from many false alarm sources
- Form C contacts, normally closed-intrusion standard, normally open-activates VCR

## Now CCTV Installers Don't Have To Compromise To Get A Quality PIR

- **Available in Color and Black & White**
- **New and improved GBC electronics**
- Unique high gain amplifier for extreme low light performance
- Higher resolution
- New backlight compensation circuit

**Visiontech** 919 Calle Amanecer Suite J., San Clemente, CA 92673 www.visiontechintl.com. Very nice distributor (or OEM not sure) CCTV lenses, auto focus – auto iris cameras, pinhole lens set ups plus they act as a distributor for KT&C Co., LTD from Korea for board cameras, "world's smallest" video camera, as well as other high grade materials.

Might be able to get some cheaper direct, but these guys come close.

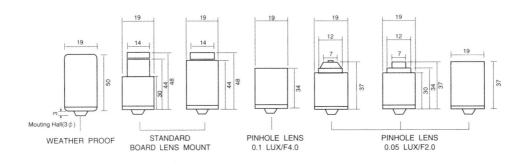

WEATHER PROOF — STANDARD BOARD LENS MOUNT — PINHOLE LENS 0.1 LUX/F4.0 — PINHOLE LENS 0.05 LUX/F2.0

## AUTO-IRIS SERIES

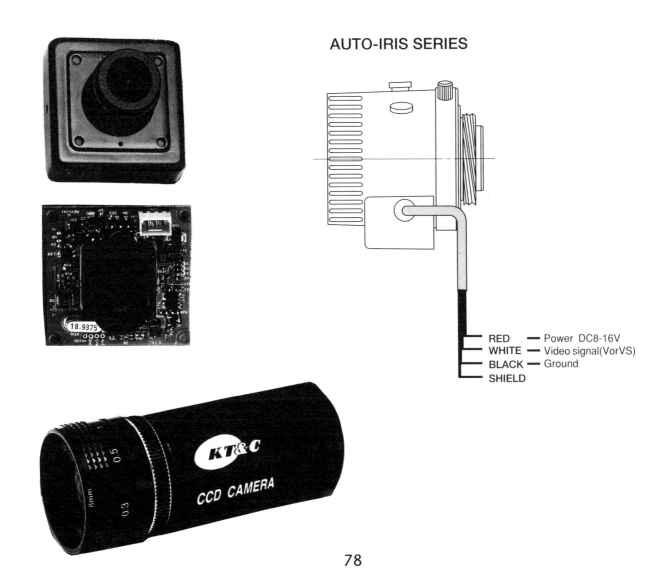

RED — Power DC8-16V
WHITE — Video signal(VorVS)
BLACK — Ground
SHIELD

**Jameco** 1355 Shoreway Rd., Belmont, CA 94002 www.jameco.com. Test and cabling equipment plus some surprising prices on video transmitters, cameras, motion detectors.

## 4-Channel 1.2 GHz Wireless Audio/Video Receiver and 20mW Transmitter

*Make your camera wireless up to 495 feet!*

- Output power: 20mW
- Output impedance: 50Ω typical
- Video input: 1Vp-p composite video, BNC connector
- Audio input: 2Vp-p maximum
- Transmission range: 495' (150 meters) outdoors 198' (60 meters) indoors
- Jumper selectable on transmitting unit for 1-4 channels
- Built-in sound and mute function, screen time controller, channel auto scanning and channel locked function on receiver
- Receiver compatible with monitor (P/N 148501) pg 119 , and adapter (P/N 114788) pg 53
- Includes user's manual, antenna, mounting hardware for transmitter, 15V @ 500mA power supply and cables • One year warranty

**157489**
- Size: 4.0"L x 3.0"W x 1.5"H • Weight: 1.5 lbs.

**157497**
- Size: 7.5"L x 5.0"W x 1.3"H • Weight: 3.0 lbs.

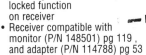

| Part No. | Description | 1-4 | 5-9 |
|---|---|---|---|
| 157489 | 4-channel transmitter | $69.95 | $62.95 |
| 157497 | 4-channel receiver | 149.95 | 134.95 |

## Infrared Lighted Camera

- Adjustable camera lens
- 6 infrared LEDs for night vision
- Auto iris controlled
- 380 TV line resolution
- Scanning frequency: 15.734kHz
- Scanning system: 2:1 interlace
- Video output: 1.0Vp-p/ 75Ω
- 0.1 lux with F2.0 • Lens: 3.6mm
- Matching connectors: RG59 BNC (P/N 71271, pg 53)
- Includes 12VDC @ 500mA power supply and wall mounting bracket • One-year warranty
- Size: 2.9"L x 2.0"W x 2.0"H • Weight: 1.5 lbs.

| Part No. | Description | Price |
|---|---|---|
| 150404 | Enclosed infrared lighted camera | $129.95 |

## JAMECO Video Transmitter Station

This powerful device transmits from a source location to any number of remote locations through TVs.

- Transmit/receive: channels 7-13
- Dual color LED function indicators
- Use with a camcorder for stereo audio sound
- Adjustment screws for volume, brightness and signal with test pattern switch
- Includes removable telescoping antenna
- Type F connector for cable & larger antennas to increase broadcast range • Includes audio & video cables
- Transmitter dimensions: 5.5"L x 3.5"W x 1.2"H
- Weight: 1.3 lbs. • One-year warranty

| Part No. | Description | 1-4 | 5-9 |
|---|---|---|---|
| 131828 | Video transmitter | $39.95 | $35.95 |

**Motron** 310 Garfield St., Suite 4, Eugene, OR 97402 www.motorn.com. A series of DTMF and controller boards, most for 2 -ways.

## TONE-MASTER™
# M-16A & TM-16A Plus
## DTMF & Rotary Test Decoders

**Manuals Plus** POB 549 Tooele, UT 84074 www.manualsplus.com. A great source for test equipment manuals; Tektronix, Fluke, HP, Triplett and hundreds of others.

**Electronic Security Products, Inc.,** POB 20545 New York, NY 10021. Off the shelf covert video products plus a couple of really nice original products such as their pen and sunglasses.

The glasses place the front element of the camera in the nose bridge and transfers the signal down the "croakies". Both units available in color or b and w, with/without audio.

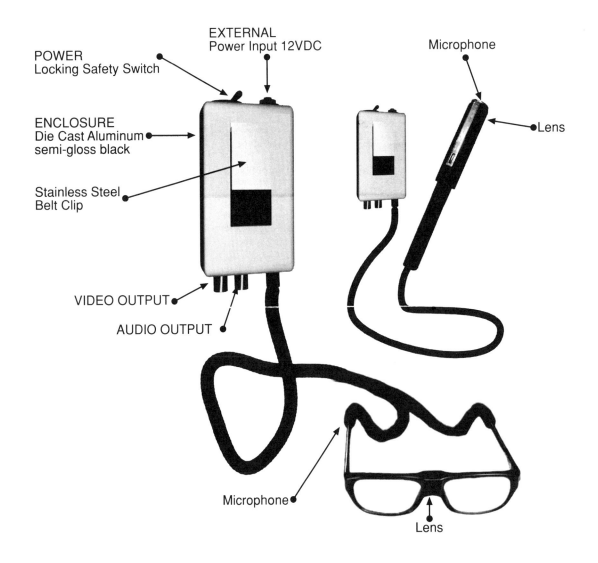

POWER
Locking Safety Switch

EXTERNAL
Power Input 12VDC

Microphone

ENCLOSURE
Die Cast Aluminum
semi-gloss black

Lens

Stainless Steel
Belt Clip

VIDEO OUTPUT

AUDIO OUTPUT

Microphone

Lens

**Ramtronics Co., Ltd.,** POB 55-273 Taipei, Taiwan. OEM 2.4 GHz transmitters, 4 channel receivers, PIR/wireless cameras/transmitter combos.

# Digital Video Surveillance

**Receiver**

**Remote Controller**
*(Optional)*

**Transmitter**

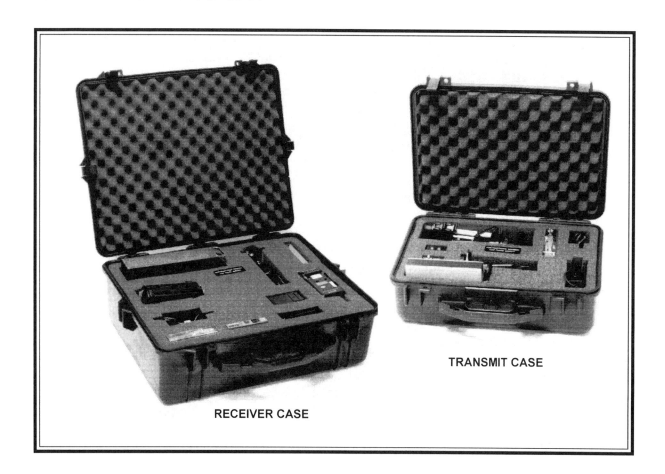

TRANSMIT CASE

RECEIVER CASE

## "GRAB & GO"

*Complete video surveillance system packaged in two cases
ready for technical operations personnel to "Grab & Go"*

**Northern Telepresence Corp.,** POB 267 Cambridge, VT 05444. A unique stand alone covert video system that combines a Watec camera and a Sony ZBOX VCR in a Pelican case.

The unit, dubbed the Sentinel VS-14 is designed to be left alone for up to 30 days (more with optional solar power panels) anywhere one feels the action may be comin'.

To.

The Sentinel will wake up and record when a person or vehicle approaches from 5 to 500 feet (depending on the trigger chosen), record the action for any selected duration, time and date stamp the footage, and then go back to sleep.

The neatest thing about the Sentinel are the available options: trigger the process with a wireless PIR trigger (included with the system) pressure mat, tape switch (can be buried or camouflaged) movement switch, seismic detectors (wireless) pager (in which one ties one's pager into the system and then pages one's self to activate Mr. Sentinel) photo beam trigger or "specialty" triggers.

One can also add a video link module for wireless transmission, a cell communication module that will automatically dial the user with a pre-recorded message, IR illuminators, thermal imagers, other cameras...

**Eye-Q Systems** 9230 Deering Ave., Chatsworth, CA 91311 www.eyeqsys.com. Cameras, transmitters, receivers, recorders, boosters, amps, antennas. Resellers but fairly complete selection.

## Cameras ◆ Transmitters
## Receivers ◆ Recorders
## Boosters, Amps & Antennas
### for Professional & Personal needs

- ✓ **Professional Law Enforcement**
- ✓ **Home Theft & Burglary**
- ✓ **Retail Loss Prevention**
- ✓ **Nanny Watch for Abuse & Negligence**
- ✓ **Industrial Espionage**
- ✓ **Inventory Theft**
- ✓ **Safety & Accident Fraud**
- ✓ **Shoplifting**
- ✓ **Subrosa Investigations**
- ✓ **Sting Operations**
- ✓ **Mobile Surveillance**
- ✓ **Portable Monitoring: Home & Office**

### INTRODUCING
# VBC-2000
## BRIEFCASE VIDEO RECEIVER-RECORDER

*This all-in-one briefcase unit breaks the barriers of video* **transmission and recording***: easy-to-carry, already disguised and hi-tech:* **perfect portability for a variety of covert surveillance needs**.

**Kings Security Inc.**, POB 41924 Fayetteville, NC 28309. Semi-custom supplier of title 3 and some "civilian" goodies include a "KSI Remote Video Surveillance System", a portable wireless or wired self contained high resolution recording system, a very, very useful "video adapter" audio pre-amplifier microphone battery pack designed to be used with any pinhole type camera, a video cell phone, video in a 2 x 4 board and in a piece of "asphalt".

KSI "big lens" is a 100mm to 500mm manual zoom lens with a camera adapter and low light, hi-res video camera. Read a vehicle tag at 500 yards, face at 350 or add a 2X booster for an equivalent 5000mm lens.

Also video helmet, transmitter and phone line sender.

Seen the stuff, met the owner. Very nice, very professional.

**Total Recall Corporation** 50A South Main Street, Spring Valley, NY 10977 www.TotalRecallcorp.com. Very slick OEM of composite systems plus good prices on Sony, Litton. American Dynamics products. Designed for law enforcement or good PI's, TC gives bang for the buck.

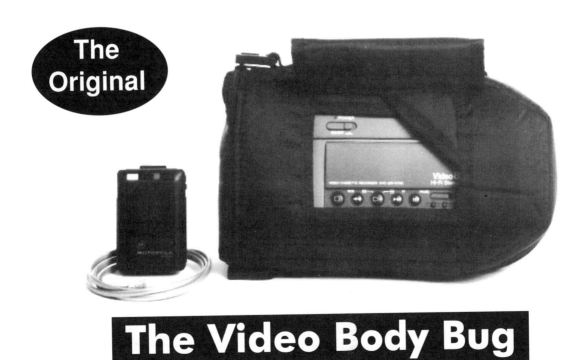

The Original

**The Video Body Bug**

**Gadgets By Design** 325 S. Washington, Lansing, MI 48933 www.jeffhall.com. Watec camera/transmitter system, several receiver/recorder combos.

### WC 500 Wireless Camera & Receiver

This is a amazing break-through product in the Wireless transmitter and camera systems. The WC 500 is a rugged yet high performance camera with 1/3 inch CCD image sensor,250K pixels and a Horizontal resolution of 380 TV lines. Low light performance is a remarkable Minimum illumination of 0.5 lux. Comes with 3.6mm auto iris lens and antenna Transmitter Output level is 16dBm, 70 mW, 50 Operating on Frequency 471.25 MHz Cameras Power supply 12V DC (120mA) Which allows Battery operation anywhere. Camera and transmitter Dimension are a tiny 38mm(W) x 43mm(H) x39mm(L) 1.49 x 1.77 x2.32 inches This system is in use by Law Enforcement And Security Companies around the world. System includes Camera/Transmitter , Receiver Antennas and easy operating intructions.Please Contact us with any questions or concerns regarding your special applications.

**Quantity:** [ 0 ▼] **Price: $1550.00**

### LET US HELP YOU DESIGN YOUR OWN CUSTOM SYSTEM

Let us help you design your own unique surveillance system. The products on this site can be built in to an unlimited number of designs. Don't see a camera or transmitters that fits you needs, then please call us and we can help you design a system. Custom design with out the Custom Pricing.

**Quantity:** [ 0 ▼] **Price: $CALL**

**Spy Mart** POB 2327 Acworth, GA 30102 www.spymart.com. One of the most established spy shops around – REI countermeasures, Dan Gibson, etc.

**Investigative Mechanics Inc.**, 34 Gansevoort St., New York, NY 10014 www.covert1.com. Nicely thought out and constructed systems for unusual recording situations. Utilized by a number of nosy TV shows, cop sting operations, PI investigations and of course, the rock group Aerosmith.

## Investigative Mechanics Inc.

*IM/PRESS-*

Investigative Mechanics/Personal Recording Electronic Surveillance System. This is the out-of-the-box, ready-to-roll, complete bodywear system, that has become *the choice* of the top I teams & investigative units around the world! Field-tested for the past 6 months by our Operative Unit with *great success, IM/PRESS* systems are currently in use on several long term, elite team investigations you *will* see and read about in the near future. When fitted correctly this custom bodyworn undercover system offers the simple, reliable & undetectable operation we've all been waiting for, including a *true one-touch record* remote control that gives you new confidence and peace of mind. This is a *system* that gives you the ability to *concentrate on your investigation*, not your hardware- while also saving tape, batteries, and editing time!

This system is available in several different camera versions; GlassesCam, PenCam, MavCam, TieCam, Cardcam, or CustomCam. Each IM/PRESS System includes;
-Custom Body Harness(S,M,L,X), Your choice of Camera, AVM-10 Mini Hi8 VCR, RC-10 AVM vibrating, remote LED ext. cable, TFT 1.8" color monitor, micro FET lav mic, all accessories.

Video surveillance does not fall under the same general go-no go laws as does audio surveillance but a number of states are tightening the perimeters governing video surveillance even as we speak.

There is also a federal law about expectation of privacy, which states, roughly, that if a person is in a situation where there is an expectation of privacy they can sue or even take criminal action of you violate this principal.

I have heard the law explained that if you are making love on a hotel balcony you have no EOP – on the other hand, inside the room with the shades drawn is a different kettle of fish.

Talk to a lawyer.

**Everspring Industry Co Ltd.**, 2F, No. 50 Chung Hua Rd., Section 1, Tucheng City, Taipei Country, Taiwan www.everspring.com. Not sure these units have even made it into the spy shop catalogs yet – get one directly from the manufacturer.

Two models of "plug in and go" cameras that report directly to your TV or VCR, both have low light LED boosters, and audio transmission. Model C702 includes built-in PIR motion detection and an auto VCR recording trigger.

Built in mainland China.

**Eskan Electronics Ltd.,** 168 Caledonian Rd., London N1 0SQ, UK. Besides their covert audio selection EE is an OEM of high end, very sophisticated, video systems.

Fairly expensive but good stuff.

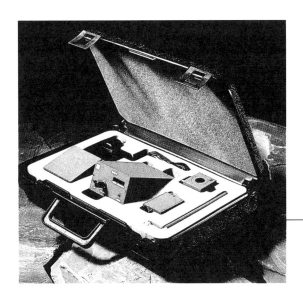

## KIT ONE

A COMPLETE KIT FOR STATIC OR MOBILE
OPERATIONS CONTAINING:
VIDEO TRANSMITTER (EVT55)
SINGLE CHANNEL VIDEO RECEIVER (EVRX1C)
B/W CAMERA (BWC1)
PATCH ANTENNA
RIGHT-ANGLE DIPOLE ANTENNA
DIPOLE ANTENNA
SWITCH MODE POWER SUPPLY
CONNECTING LEADS

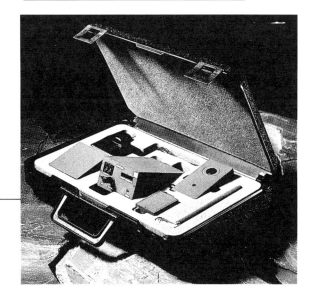

## KIT TWO

A COMPLETE KIT FOR STATIC OR MOBILE
OPERATIONS CONTAINING:
VIDEO TRANSMITTER (EVT55)
100-CHANNEL VIDEO RECEIVER (EVRX100C)
COLOUR CAMERA(LCC3)
PATCH ANTENNA
RIGHT-ANGLE DIPOLE ANTENNA
DIPOLE ANTENNA
SWITCH MODE POWER SUPPLY
CONNECTING LEADS

**Sunkwang Electronics Co. Ltd.,** 157-7 Chuni-dong, Wonmi-ku, Kyunggi-do, Korea www.chollian.net~skcoltd. Camera modules – boards, domes, lipstick, waterproof and security. 120 hour delivery, great prices.

**Advanced Electronics Group Inc.,** POB 642057 Los Angeles, CA 90064 www.aegi.com. OEM of covert surveillance systems as well as custom designed systems, AEG also distributes Sony, Panasonic, Computar, RF-Link, Trango, Digi-Spec, VideoComm, etc.

A very complete line of CVV as well as some nice optics, recorders and so on. Very good prices, some just above or at the same level as the manufacturer. Catalog $5.00, you should have one on hand.

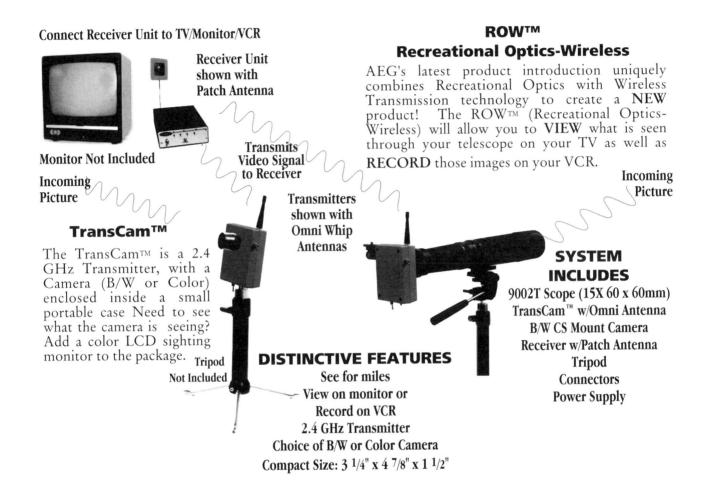

Connect Receiver Unit to TV/Monitor/VCR

Receiver Unit shown with Patch Antenna

Monitor Not Included

Incoming Picture

Transmits Video Signal to Receiver

## TransCam™

The TransCam™ is a 2.4 GHz Transmitter, with a Camera (B/W or Color) enclosed inside a small portable case Need to see what the camera is seeing? Add a color LCD sighting monitor to the package.

Tripod Not Included

Transmitters shown with Omni Whip Antennas

**DISTINCTIVE FEATURES**
See for miles
View on monitor or
Record on VCR
2.4 GHz Transmitter
Choice of B/W or Color Camera
Compact Size: 3 1/4" x 4 7/8" x 1 1/2"

## ROW™
## Recreational Optics-Wireless

AEG's latest product introduction uniquely combines Recreational Optics with Wireless Transmission technology to create a **NEW** product! The ROW™ (Recreational Optics-Wireless) will allow you to **VIEW** what is seen through your telescope on your TV as well as **RECORD** those images on your VCR.

Incoming Picture

**SYSTEM INCLUDES**
9002T Scope (15X 60 x 60mm)
TransCam™ w/Omni Antenna
B/W CS Mount Camera
Receiver w/Patch Antenna
Tripod
Connectors
Power Supply

**SpyTech** 2028 Yonge St., Toronto, CA M4S 1Z9. Another example of a left-over spy store. Minox cameras, JVC recorders, Dan Gibson Mics, Panasonic VCR's, mini board camera(s) the usual "hidden in a smoke detector-exit sign" video transmitters plus some Japanese products at a very high markup.

**Command Corporation** POB 832 East Granby, CT 06026. "Wireless video that really works" – these nice people sell FBI grade transmitters, receivers, directional antennas at direct-from-the-manufacturer prices. They even occasionally feature Macy's type White Flower Day 50% sales.

High power, long distance, broadcast quality stuff. Will rent to, well, to people they want to rent to...

Some products restricted to "U.S. Government and friendly foreign governments only".

Always be a friend.

**American Innovations, Inc.**, 119 Rockland Center, Suite 315 Nannuet, NY 10954. Cameras hidden in the usual paraphernalia, a couple of wireless systems.

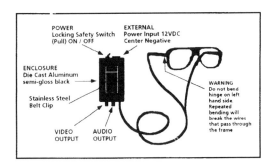

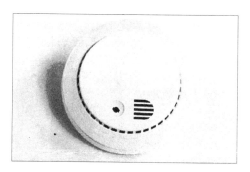

**Micro Technology Services, Inc.**, 1819 Firman Drive, Suite 137, Richardson, TX 75081 www.mitsi.com. Design, development and manufacturing of a variety of on-shelf and custom video surveillance products. A couple of nice stand alone alert-recorder systems.

Micro Technology's new Covert Video Surveillance Systems utilizes the advanced features of the SR-71 Surveillance Recorder, combined with a wireless camera and triggering device.

The SR-71 can be pre-programmed to record only when activated by the wireless motion detector, reducing the review time of boring video tape. The locations of the recorded events are stored in memory for easy review. These professional quality systems have user friendly on-screen setup menus.

**Supercircuits** One Supercircuits Plaza, Leander, TX 78641. A few years back SC became known for putting micro video cameras and transmitters in remote controlled vehicles (ATV's, model planes, helicopters, even a submarine). These models could, and did, actually transmit live video from wherever the operator guided them.

Since then SC has expanded their line to carry cameras, recorders, pinhole kits and just about anything one can think of in covert video. They also began designing their own gear and as such have some great gain antennas which can increase the range of "300'" wireless units to well over a mile. Also designed their own super small transmitters, camera systems. Really good prices. Catalog $5.00.

# NEW MICROPLATE VIDEO TRANSMITTER

We asked the designer of our Powerplate ATV video transmitters to come up with a low cost, high performance, but extremely tiny video transmitter. The result is the amazing Microplate video transmitter. It combines micro size, solid performance and low price. Weight is only 1/2 ounce and size is super tiny...only 2" X 1.25" by .16" thick. This transmitter is so small and so thin that when people see it for the first time, they can't believe it <u>is</u> a video transmitter. Transmitting frequency is 434 MHz (ATV Band), which means it can be received by any cable ready television at channel 59, or just below UHF channel 14 on most slide rule type analog tuning portable or pocket televisions. Rock solid stability is provided by an advanced Surface Acoustical Wave (SAW) resonator circuit. Until very recently, transmitters using this type of design cost hundreds more.

Do not confuse this transmitter with inferior designs being sold elsewhere. Range is up to 700 feet with standard antenna and over 2500 feet line of sight with a Yagi type antenna. Output power is 200 milliwatts and power requirement is 12 volts DC at 100 milliamps. One tiny AAA battery pack will give you hours of crystal clear video! Built tough in thinline metal housing. Comes complete with pre-installed power and video cables, and flexible 6.5" whip antenna. Also available with audio. Audio version is same size, but .35" thick.

*Comes with pre-installed video, audio and power cables, 6.5" flexible whip antenna, easy connection instructions and 1 year warranty.*

**MP-1 Microplate ATV Video Transmitter** ................................................................**$199.95**

**Toshiba America Information Systems Inc.,** 9740 Irvine Blvd., Irvine, CA 92618. OEM of the infamous "lipstick camera" and other high end broadcast quality cameras.

**Carol Products** 1750 Brielle Ave., Ocean, NJ 07712. Watec cameras and transmitters, board cameras, complete systems in sport bags and on live bodies, pinhole lens selection, monitors, recorders, etc.

Very nice, very complete line.

## WIRELESS CAMERAS

**WAT 510**      **$1345.00**

TRANSMITTER/CAMERA

Ultra Miniature 1/3" Black & White Wireless Camera with Built In Lens. For Law Enforcement, Gov't, or Export only. (5 mm or 3.6 mm Auto Iris) 12V DC. Transmission Distance 300' antenna included

**WAT 510RX**      **$785.00**

RECEIVER FOR WAT 510

Utilizing the WAT510RX Receiver with the WAT510 Wireless Camera enables the user to utilize any industry standard video monitor.

## WIRELESS TRANSMITTERS

**WA01**      **$280.00**

LOW COST RF TRANSMITTER

Audio and Video transmits approximately 300' - 500'. FCC approved. 2.4 Ghz. Compatible with any CCTV equipment. Great value.

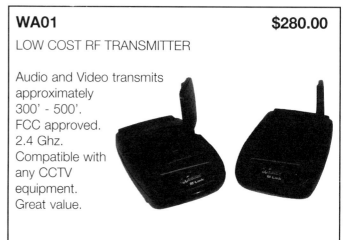

**Hanse Electronics Co., Ltd.,** 33-4 NamDong Ind, Zone 613-3 NamChon-Dong, NamDong-Gu InChon-Shi 405-100 Korea. A good manufacturer of board cams, display modules and lenses that attach to same.

Once again, save 500% (is that semantically possible?) by ordering direct...

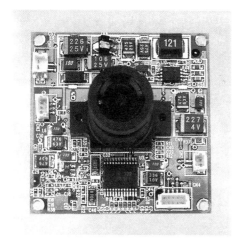

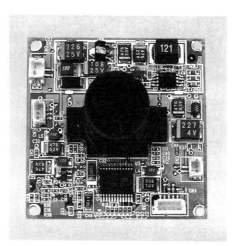

**CA-061N/P-B92**     **CA-061N/P-P60**     **CA-061N/P-CM**

**VideoComm Technologies** 407 Speers Rd., Suite 203, Oakville, Ont L6K 3T5 Canada. OEM of both 900 MHz and 2.4 GHz tiny video transmitters. Most dual power with optional audio; these units have just been introduced to the marketplace and I have received excellent reports on their performance. Low to moderate pricing. Buy direct...

## MiniSpyCam-900

## B & W Camera & Transmitter Combo

Sends real time, high resolution, B&W, NTSC or PAL, video and audio signals

- Range up to 1,000 feet Line of Sight
- Smallest pin hole camera and transmitter combo on the market
- Size: only 1.37" x 2.1" x 0.65"
- Portable, Temporary and Covert Surveillance
- Operates on 9 – 14 Volt DC
- 9 Volt Battery lasts 2 hours
- Power draw of 130 mA @ 9V and 160mA @ 12V
- Optional Audio
- AA Battery Pack Holder and 12 Volt DC Adapter included
- Choose one of two Frequencies
- Requires 900MHz Receiver — not included

## T-900

## Shrink-Wrap Transmitter

Sends real time, high resolution, color & B&W, NTSC or PAL, video and audio signals.

- Range up to 1,000 feet (Low Power) Line of Sight
- Range up to 2,000 feet (High Power) Line of Sight
- Smallest 900MHz transmitter on the market - size of a quarter
- OEM or custom configure your own wireless camera system
- Power draw of 40 mA @ 9 V and 56 mA @ 12 V
- Transmitter Size: only 1.1" x 0.9"
- Optional Audio Line Level or Microphone (Law Enforcement)
- Operates on 9 – 14 Volt DC
- Choose one of two Frequencies
- Requires 900MHz Receiver — not included

**Q Enterprises** POB 234 Landing, NJ 07850. Good selection of other people's goods – Watec cameras, lot's of Asian board cameras some hidden in clocks, plants, ties, thermostats, telephones, coffeepots you name it.

Also rentals, leases, custom design.

**First Witness Video Surveillance Systems** Old Town Hall Bldg., Route 11 South, Mt. Sidney, VA 24467. Designed primarily for law enforcement FW puts together a variety of body systems, stand alone units that activate on different triggers, VCR's with built-in motion detectors, and cameras, cameras in houseplants, pinholes etc.

Stakeout Partner

- **Complete self contained recording system with _video_ motion detector, hidden camera, event recorder, phone dialer and wireless remote activation.**

- **Perfect for areas of larceny or for reoccurring B & E's.**

- **VCR stays in "Standby Mode" so there is no "Dead" time on the tape.**

- **12VDC operation.**

**Aegis Research** 186-196 West Broadway, Vancouver, B.C., V6S 1J8 Canada. OEM of what probably legitimately the smallest video transmitters in the world Aegis offers two different units (two different power levels) both draw power directly from a nine volt battery and broadcast directly to any cable ready TV receiver (cable channel 59).

The units are a little larger than a quarter and do a good job of throwing a video signal to a nearby television receiver.

Sold for much over cost from a number of spy suppliers.

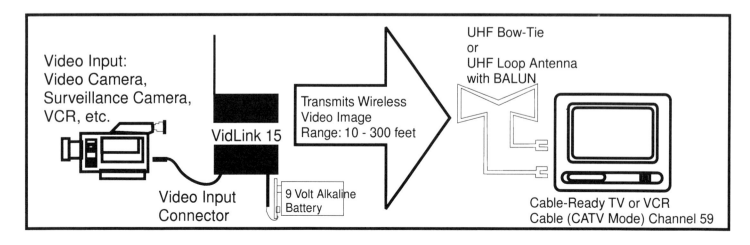

**Viking International** 150 Executive Park Blvd., #4600, San Francisco, CA 94134. Viking is owned and operated by a very good engineer, most of their products are designed and manufactured in-house.

Prices are very good as is their equipment which includes phantom powered mini mics, amplifiers, compressors, IR "tags", long play recorders, an IR probe which will find and demodulate laser eavesdropping attacks, countermeasures gear and some of the best video transmitters I've tested.

The VIR 900 Professional Video Receiver is designed to be used with the VI 900 series of video transmitters.

The VIR 900 is color-capable and uses state of the art GaAs semiconductors, SAW technology and surface mount construction for high reliability.

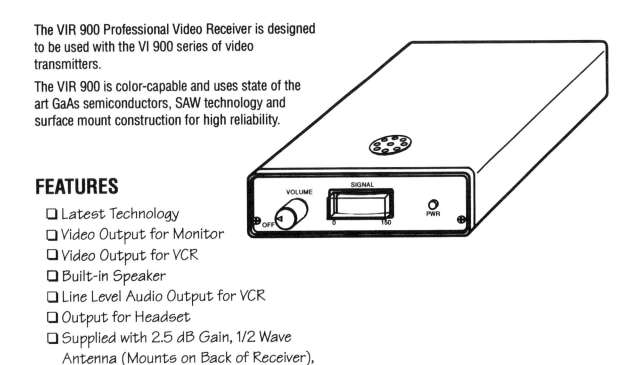

# FEATURES

❑ Latest Technology
❑ Video Output for Monitor
❑ Video Output for VCR
❑ Built-in Speaker
❑ Line Level Audio Output for VCR
❑ Output for Headset
❑ Supplied with 2.5 dB Gain, 1/2 Wave
   Antenna (Mounts on Back of Receiver),
   AC Adapter, and Car Cord

# APPLICATIONS

Covert marking of:

• Runways
• Landing Zones
• Drop Zones
• Personnel
• Vehicles, Boats, Aircraft

Other Applications:

• Covert Signalling
• Tracking of Cargo

# SPECIAL CHARACTERISTICS

• Visible Through Clothing

**NightFlash Infrared Marker Beacon with Battery**

**Coherent Communications Inc.**, 28245 Avenue Crocker, Suite 200, Valencia, CA 91355. American made transmitters, receivers, gain antennas and complete systems. Wide variety of gear from medium priced transmitters up to and including units designed for the broadcast industry.

CC's units are FM, as opposed to the lower priced AM units sold by virtually every "spy" company. Known for their range, clarity and stability, CC's are worth the extra cost.

Also a nifty walkie-talkie based unit that will control a camera (turn on, pan, tilt, zoom) from as far as five miles away.

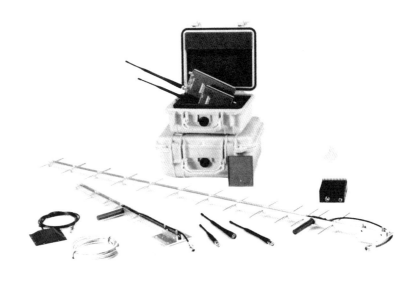

**Wetedh Electronics Co. Ltd.**, 35-3 Wonmi-Dong, Wonmi-gu, Bucheon-city, Kyeongki-do, Korea. 5 board cameras, several domes and even one miniature (WM-500DC) digital C mount unit.

**Spy Tech** 2028 Yonge St., Toronto, Ont M4S 1Z9 Canada. Reseller of concealed video cameras, a transmitter or two.

# WIRELESS VIDEO TRANSMISSION

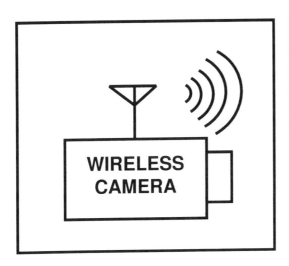

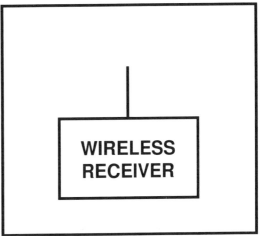

**P-Squared Communications** 117 Mount Penn Road, Shillington, PA 19607 www.p2comm.com. Distributes the Alliant line of wireless video systems in the United States.

**CCS** 360 Madison Ave., 6th Floor, NY 10017. Expensive resellers, slick ($25) catalog. Got in some trouble a few years back and turned all their customers over to the FBI...

# 2400 PORTABLE VIDEO TRANSMISSION SYSTEMS

**Wireless Technology Inc.**, 7340 Smoke Ranch Road, Suite A, Las Vegas, NV 89128 www.wirelesstech.com. Besides the only in-your-ear radio receiver, WT makes video transmission systems for LE and upper end investigators.

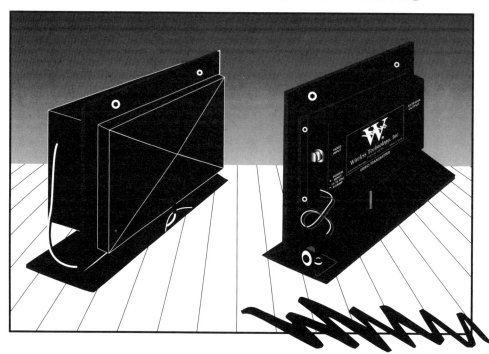

he Wireless Technology 2400 Portable Video Surveillance System is recognized as the industry leader in system portability, video clarity and installation flexibility. It is the solution for the most challenging installations that require swift deployment for long or short surveillance operations.

## SLEEK DESIGN. SWIFT DEPLOYMENT.

The sleek and compact design of the versatile system allows you to capture video imagery discreetly. The portable receiver and transmitter can be placed or mounted anywhere and relocated quickly and easily. It transmits realtime video images as clearly from an airborne helicopter as it will from an undercover drug sting. Its versatility is also enhanced by the variety and simplicity of power options available. The 2400 Portable System derives power from portable battery packs to AC/DC power adapters.

## SUPERIOR RECEPTION. SHARP CLARITY.

**Jumbo Hardware Co., Ltd.**, No. 3 Lane 76, Hsi Yuan Rd., Wu-Ku, Taipei, Taiwan. Sort of a neighborhood hardware store by mail, except they also stock 5 wireless video transmission systems.

he Wireless Technology 2400 Portable Video Surveillance transmitter and receiver are designed to function with a variety of antennas; each system can be customized to provide the best video reception for each installation. For greater distance or high gain, high-performance point-to-point directional antennas are used. For shorter distances, low gain, wider beamwidth antennas are used. The antennas are designed to complement the compact size of the 2400 Portable System and can be as small as a matchbook.

And to further insure superior reception, the powerful 2400 Portable System can transmit through airwave interference and "noise" with multi-channel operation.

Contact your Wireless Technology, Inc. representative to see how the 2400 Portable System can meet your video surveillance needs.

Electronic Equipment Bank 323 Mill St., Vienna, VA 22180. www.access.digex.net/~eeb./eeb.html. Communication supplier (see entry in Communications section) plus some very useful gear for surveillance or TSCM work.

# SR-3555a Wide Band Surveillance

The SR-3555A Surveillance System offers a wide range of capabilities at a surprising low cost. The basic unit is completely portable and can be configured for a number of different applications. The major components (receiver and spectral display) are commercial-off-the-shelf (COTS) units repackaged for portability.

The system includes an interface panel where all external connections are made (power, digital, audio, video and RF). A variable RF attenuator is also installed here to provide better control of the signal levels into the receiver.

The AR-3000A Receiver offers wide coverage, .1-2036 MHz. With a high level of performance and versatility from long wave through shortwave, VHF and toward the upper limit of UHF, coupled with a state of the art spectrum display unit which is the first to use a 16 color LCD screen. Up to 10MHz of spectrum can be displayed. Control of the receiver can be accomplished from the key pad of the display. By moving the SDU5000 cursor left or right, or pressing the PEAK key, you can pinpoint a signal of interest and instantly the receiver will jump that station and will display frequency and signal strength in dBM. All data can be stored on the disk for later analysis if a personal computer is used as the controller. The SDU5000 features an easy to use menu driven format. The video output of the SDU (either NTSC or PAL format) can be connected to larger video monitors for presentation to groups or be recorded on a VCR.

**System Specifications:**
**Input Power:** Available from internal 12 volt system battery (4 hour battery life). Charging unit included.
**Size:** 46 x 38 x 18cm (18 x 17 x 7 inch)
**Weight:** Approx. 10kg (22lbs.)

Priced from: **$3955**

> **NOW AVAILABLE...SR5555 BUILT AROUND THE NEW AR5000 STARTING AT $5955**

Transcrypt International 4800 Northwest 1st Street, Lincoln, NE 68521. www.transcrypt.com. Although not designed for surveillance, Transcrypt makes a small unit which turns hand held and mobile radios into repeaters.

This allows one to place a low powered bug or tap on premises and then have the signal picked up and re-braodcast to a distant receiver using conventional radios.

# TRANSPEATER™

The Transpeater turns two portable or mobile two-wat radios into an instant repeater or cross band system, allowing conventional repeater operation or bi-directional relay operation.

Telewave, Inc. 1155 Terra Bella Ave., Mountain View, CA 94043. www.telewaveinc.com. Industrial supplier of municipal trunked radio accessories, cell site antennas and a couple of directional antennas that can be used for cell phone interception.

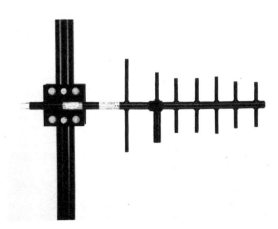

**Aspect Technology and Equipment Inc.,** 811 E. Plano Prky., Plano TX 75074. Known primarily for their selection of OP's night vision equipment, Aspect also offers a number of video cameras, lenses, editing boards and cases.

---

## QUASI TIME LAPSE ADAPTER FOR SONY VIDEO CASSETTE RECORDERS (PGV-220) ATE/VCR1002

* Provides Quasi Time Lapse Capability for the Sony GV-S50 and EVO-220
  - Provides Alarm Recording
  - Provides Timed Recording
  - Easily Attaches to Sony Recorders

**Quark Video Surveillance Systems,** 537 Third Ave., New York, NY 10016 www.quarkfiles.com. High end reseller of hidden video systems (pens, telephones, smoke detectors, etc.). Caters to people with a large budget and no on-site technician, well I guess that would be *law enforcement*.

Nice catalog.

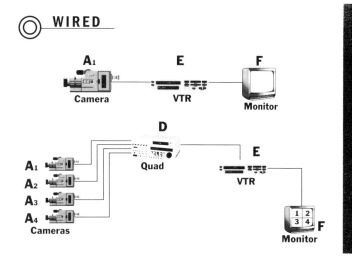

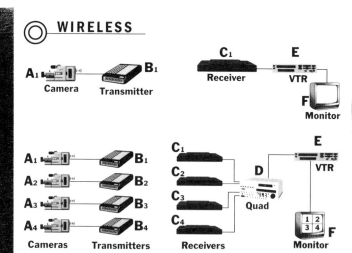

**All Phase Video Security** 70 Cain Dr., Brentwood, NY 11717. A "wholesale video warehouse" that will sell retail. Hundreds of products ranging from CCTV security and dome cameras, Sony, Toshiba, GYYR time lapse recorders, a couple of pinhole units, a few board cameras, GBC hidden cameras, cable, tools.

Prices are some of the best in the business.

**Shadow Security Products** 5686 Lone Pine Road, Sebastopol, CA 95472. Video sunglasses, video pen, and briefcase.

Captured images can be recorded in real time using a standerd video recorder or fed into a video transmitter for remote parallel surveillance and/or recording.

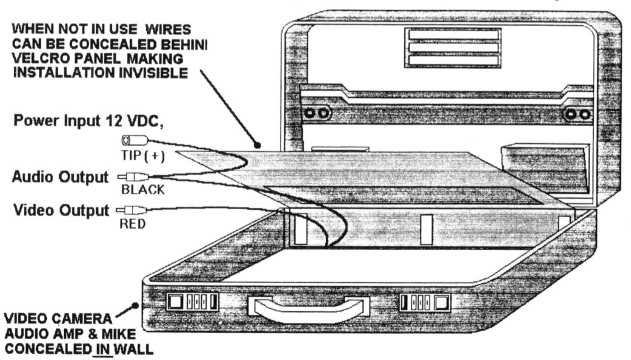

WHEN NOT IN USE WIRES CAN BE CONCEALED BEHINI VELCRO PANEL MAKING INSTALLATION INVISIBLE

Power Input 12 VDC,
TIP ( + )

Audio Output
BLACK

Video Output
RED

VIDEO CAMERA AUDIO AMP & MIKE CONCEALED IN WALL

*"Unique Video Instrumentation"*

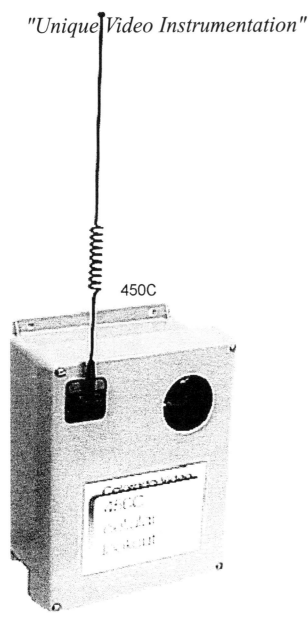

450C

**Colorado Video** POB 928 Boulder, CO 80306 www.colorado-video.com. OEM of a variety of video processing and viewing equipment. Primary business is wholesale to dealers but they will sell directly to customers.

Of particular interest to security and investigative types are their models of remote camera systems (solar powered) that will take an image when the operator triggers it by means of a cellular call, grab an image when triggered by an external alarm and call the operator (transmitting said image(s) over the cell network) or a combination of the above.

## Cellular Lookout Remote Camera System Model 450

Colorado Video's Cellular Lookout is a family of solar powered cameras that use cellular technology to transmit pictures from remote sites where AC power and hard-wire communications channels are not readily available.

### A Choice of Operating Modes

Three versions of the Cellular Lookout are available. A call to the Model 450A causes it to acquire and send a picture to its companion receiver, Model 451A. Alternatively, the Model 450B places a call and transmits a picture upon external trigger. Model 450C combines these functions. Transmission of the picture to the receiver for display on a video monitor requires only 32 seconds.

---

**Racewood Technology Co., Ltd.,** 4F, 480-4, Sec. 6, Yen Ping N. Rd., Taipei, Taiwan ROC 11163.

- 900, 1200,1300 and 2.4 GHz audio/video observation system with four available channels
- Same only wireless
- 2-way integrated surveillance control system (coax)
- Color processor
- "Combined security system to CATV system with modulator"

Inexpensive, easy to use.

---

**Spyworld, Inc.**, 311 South Division St., Carson City, NV 89703 wwwspyworld.com. OPS, fairly basic, a product or two I can't source.

Wrist Watch Camera

Telephone Tap Detector

**Canwood Products** POB 585 Beumont, CA 92223. Minimal line to avoid putting the customer thru the nightmare of too many choices.

## Miniature Video Camera with Audio

- Color & B&W Mini-Surveillance Cameras...
- Wide Angle Lens...Built-in Microphone...
- Color Cam has 230 TV Lines of Resolution...
- Black & White has 380 TV Lines of Resolution...
- 2" x 2-1/2" x 1"...
- Mount Anywhere...25' of Cable Included...
- AC Adapter Included..

There is a mind boggling assortment of miniature covert video cameras available on the Internet and elsewhere. We found that our customers (and we ourselves) were often confused when it came to making a decision about what type and model of camera to buy. So, to keep everything as simple as possible, we have decided to limit our selection to just one model of b&w camera and one color camera. The camera listed below is very high quality, very small size, and should cover just about any situation you would encounter that requires a camera of this type. Easy connection. Two wires connect to the RCA video in jacks of your VCR, modulator or monitor TV. This is one of the smallest and best performing miniature B&W and Color video cameras you can buy.

We also have cameras built into everyday items such as smoke detectors, pictures, speakers, radios, books, clocks, etc. or use with our VidLink miniature video transmitter for one of the smallest self contained wireless video systems available.

**Surveillance Specialties Ltd.**, 40 Chatham Way, Lynnfield, MA 01940. A licensed private investigation agency that does not commit the act of investigation. "Our specialty is covert video surveillance and that is all we do. In fact we have installed over 3000 covert camera systems in areas that range from warehouses to the executive offices of fortune 500 companies".

They supply only one product, but it's a nice one – the BRAX-1 provides a stable working platform for almost every drop ceiling installation. The flexible bracket is removable and can also be used with magnetic or screw down bases.

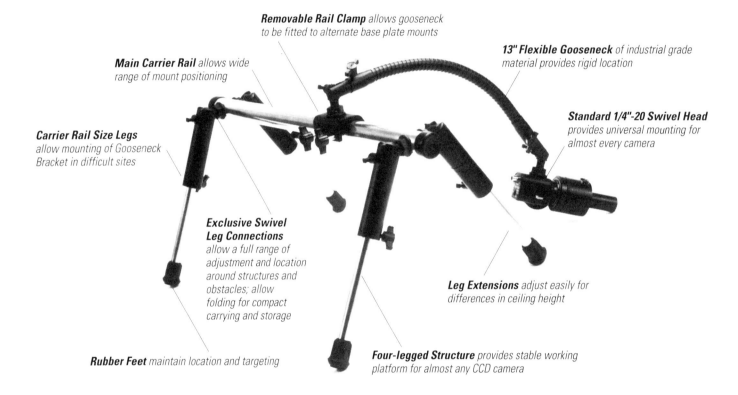

**Removable Rail Clamp** allows gooseneck to be fitted to alternate base plate mounts

**13" Flexible Gooseneck** of industrial grade material provides rigid location

**Main Carrier Rail** allows wide range of mount positioning

**Standard 1/4"-20 Swivel Head** provides universal mounting for almost every camera

**Carrier Rail Size Legs** allow mounting of Gooseneck Bracket in difficult sites

**Exclusive Swivel Leg Connections** allow a full range of adjustment and location around structures and obstacles; allow folding for compact carrying and storage

**Leg Extensions** adjust easily for differences in ceiling height

**Rubber Feet** maintain location and targeting

**Four-legged Structure** provides stable working platform for almost any CCD camera

**FM Systems** 3877 South Main Street, Santa Ana, CA 92707. At least two fairly unique items designed to enhance the capacity and capability of security and covert (coax) video systems.

Send two separate signals down the same line and/or add audio to existing installs.

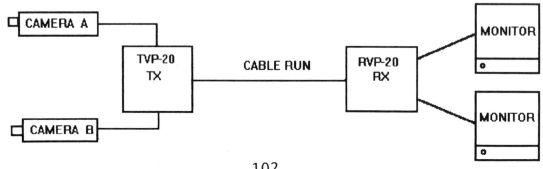

# Wireless Pole Cam—Covert Video

On the streets it's hard to gather the appropriate intelligence to put a stop on criminal activity. For urban areas, it's essential to monitor critical street activities covering a wide area. Sometimes a need arises when surveillance is necessary, but not the presence of technical operation units. When discretion and secrecy are essential in outdoor surveillance, This innovative *Pole Cam* solves the surveillance problems most government agencies must overcome. The *Pole Cam* is a power line transformer look-alike. Since it looks identical to the electrical equipment found on most streetscapes, it can be mounted on a pole in any street environment and go unnoticed as video surveillance equipment.

**Tritech Associates**, Inc. 2314 Tapestry CT., Toms River, New Jersey 08755. A long time supplier to intelligence agencies, police departments and some private agencies TA does audio, does video, GPS tracking and son on and so forth.

Obviously they are not going to sell covert audio to anyone not title 3 graced, but if you be da cops they good some very nice stuff. Non title 3 gear to other folks.

Much appears OEM or at least modified; other lines include ICOM, Dan Gibson, and others.

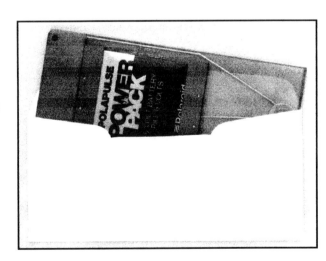

The *T-60-E* is another low profile transmitter. Envelopes are not an uncommon site around an office or in a briefcase, making this transmitter highly undetectable. The *T-60-E* has one standard channel that operates between 148-174 Mhz.

Video Countermeasures –

**Intelligence Incorporated,** 3555 S. El Camino Real, San Mateo, CA 94403 www.intelligence.to. A major black hole in the area of electronic surveillance countermeasures has been the blatant lack of equipment which will reliably detect what is probably the most common piece of surveillance gear on the market today. Exactly of what do I be speaking? Of? The ever present "nanny cam" – micro video cameras stashed in teddy bears, bedside clocks, smoke detectors, rocks, plant pots and a variety of other off the shelf objects which, coupled to a small transmitter will throw the signal 100- 500 feet (more with a gain antenna) to a down converter, monitor and video recorder. These units can be purchased from many suppliers and take advantage of the newly available, even approved by our old friends the FCC, low power video bands at 900 MHz and 2.4 GHz. As anyone who has ever tried to ferret these units out with convention countermeasures gear can tell you; she no be happenin'. In fact, testing a number of mid to top end (read $14K here) counter surveillance units failed to provide one reliable video finder. Many units claim to find video signals in these ranges, but do not come thru. A brand new unit that is designed specifically to indicate and locate video (and audio) signals in the new bands is now available. Said unit is designed by a gentleman I've known for more years than I care to admit. He has spent 20+ years designing some of the best ESCM (and, let's be honest, some ah, good to great surveillance gear) on the market with regard to operation and price.

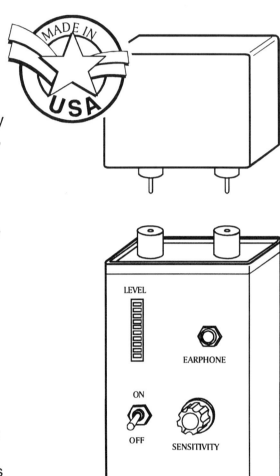

The FD-3000 video detector has a number of unique features including Advanced MMIC electronics, true RF gain control for maximum dynamic range (most units us a "detected level control" instead) State of the art Planar antenna in the RF head covers 900- 3100 MHz coupled with the best dynamic range of any detector on the market (50 Db).

**Christensen Designs** POB 348 Manteca, CA 95336. CD has just released a couple of new products worthy of consideration – a head mounted video display one wears like a virtual reality eyepiece that produces high quality video from several sources including their miniature IR probe, TreeTop viewers or "Tethered Remote Control Device."

Also very nifty IR high power Spotlight (diode) with adjustable beam control and various output powers.

**NarcOfficer** 112 State Street, Albany, NY 12207. A slick newsletter/magazine produced for those who uphold the drug laws, this publication offers articles such as *Bribery: The Drug Dealer's Best Friend* and *Combating the Loners, Drug Smuggling by Air and Sea*, as well as awards and news of the Narc community.

Actually it's a good read, I mention it because I have found two specific uses that seem to have alluded the publishers:
• Take it into your favorite dive/biker bar, order a soda water and read it. You *will* make new friends.
• Leave it on the seat of your car when parking in marginal neighborhoods and don't worry about the stereo being stolen…

**Security Products International** 30 Old Budd Lake Road, Budd Lake, NJ 07828. Has just released details of their antenna cam a very nice product for unobtrusive semi-mobile surveillance.

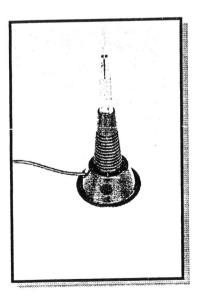

**Criminal Research Products Inc.**, POB 408 Conshohocken, PA 19428. "Birthplace of the fingerprint industry." CRP makes every conceivable type of fingerprint finder and also carries some great binoculars, flashlights and forensic lights.

**SVS–990 SCANNING CAMERA**

Features 155 degree scanning action - provides full coverage of wide areas plus added deterrent power of continuous movement. Long-life, quiet, 1RPM motor.

**Surveillance Video Systems** 258 A Street, Suite 12, Ashland, OR 97520. SVS makes a low cost "plug and go" single camera convenience store type security system as well as phony cameras that look exactly like the real thing, minus any interior components.

"No thief wants his picture taken."

Telephone

Thermostat

**Electronic Video Systems** 2029 West Woodland, Springfield, MO 65807. Inexpensive CCTV cameras, monitors, recorders from all major manufacturers.

**Super Sharp International Inc.**, 9F, No. 59, Sec. 2, Tun Hwa S. Rd., Taipei 106, Taiwan. Makes a number of CCTV (security type) cameras and wireless video systems.

**EverFocus Electronics Corp.** 10F-6 No. 79, Sec. 1, Shin-Tai Wu Rd., Hsi-Chi Taiwan 221. Complete line of video input, storage and processing equipment for security applications.

# ELECTRONIC TRACKING

**Tracking Products Inc.**, 4700 Sterling Dr., Boulder, CO 80301. OEM of several different types of electronic tracking devices these nice folks got into the business quite a few years ago designing personal transmitters and df equipment for such diverse applications as finding misplaced wildlife and wandering Alzheimer's' patients.

They make a unique covert tracking device that emits a coded burst of information several times a second that actually provides the exact direction of travel as well as some distance information from the target vehicle *itself*.

Also designed and provide one of the more effective GPS covert systems available, the Pro Trak GPS.

Sold by many dealers. Go direct.

**Vehicle tracking can now be accomplished from the privacy of your computer using the new PRO TRAK-GPS system.**

The PRO TRAK-GPS consists of a GPS Receiver and Cellular Modem (seen at right) which is fastened to the target vehicle with wire ties or is bolted securely.

A GPS "Puck" antenna attaches with a magnet to the underside of the bumper cover and a miniature mag mount cellular antenna fastens to the frame.

Power is supplied by a direct connect to vehicle power or by a field replaceable battery pack which will power the system for approximately 5 days.

The system can be accessed from a HOST PC at your office using our Host software package. The location of the target is displayed on a digital map of your area.

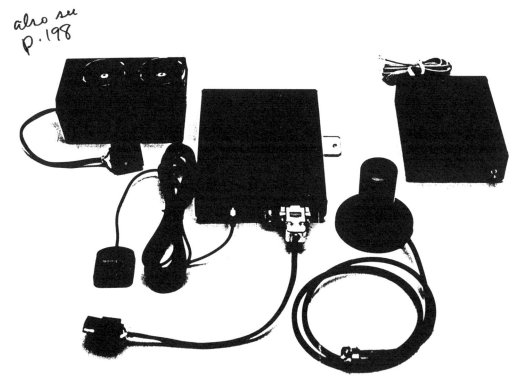

also see p. 198

**Pictured from left to right; Magnet mount power pack, GPS Puck antenna, Vehicle unit, Cellular Antenna, and Host Modem.**

**Doppler Systems** 37002 Sidewinder Road, Carefree, AZ 85377. DS has offered radio "direction finders" for a number of years. Their systems have been used for vehicle tracking, although the company has not marketed their products specifically for this application.

Until now – A unique combination of rf (four antennas) locating combined with GPS makes for a very accurate and unusual tracking system. The 6100 series can be used either covertly or overtly in conjunction with almost any transmitter from inexpensive "beepers" to cell phones, providing electronic tracking and/or target (with GPS) location.

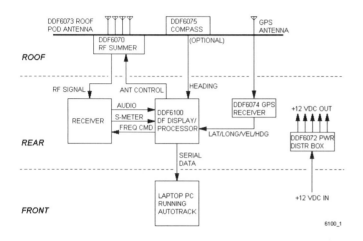

The 6100 SERIES RADIO DIRECTION FINDER provides a self contained system for mobile triangulation. Utilizing the AutoTrack software program running on the user's laptop computer, lines of bearing may be recorded on a digital map. A GPS receiver is used to measure the tracking vehicle's location and heading which are displayed as an icon on the map. Lines of bearing (LOB) are also shown on the map originating from the icon. When the user determines that a valid bearing is displayed, the LOB is stored and the icon changes. By driving to another location and taking another LOB, the intersection indicating the emitter location is found. This process continues as the tracking vehicle closes on the emitter. The number of LOBs displayed may be limited to show only the most recent, however, all selected LOB data is written to a file that may be recovered later for analysis of the data.

**StarTrac, Inc.** 3575 Beltline Road Suite 347 Irving, TX Offers a lease-rent-purchase option on a covert GPS system, in most parts of the US.

Utilizing approximately the same sized unit, same accuracy as the II and Shadow, one rents the actual equipment and then simply call into the nice people at StarTrac to set up your service requirements, which can include on-demand locating, automatic notification, real time surveillance, notify client when vehicle reaches or leaves a particular target area.

Rates vary from about $900 (includes equip rental for 3 months, insurance and activation) to half that figure on a one year lease.

One then also pays $0.50 per locate request, $4.00 for specialized maps, $5.00 per daily reports, $4.00 per on-demand locate etc.

With StarTrac one can also get (uh, pay for) on-line tech support, unit installation, investigator's time and other interesting implants.

**Kings Security Inc.,** POB 41924 Fayetteville, NC 28309. Very nice, very tiny tracking transmitter that can be person, vehicle or parcel applied and then followed with a directional antenna or more expensive df equipment.

Also both active and passive GPS covert systems for investigators.

STANDARD TRACKING TRANSMITTER

Florida based Pro Tech Monitoring www.ptm.com has developed a GPS based tracking system called the SMART system which puts a tamperproof ankle bracelet on criminal offenders which contains a portable tracking device electronically linked to a GPS receiver and cellular communicator.

Unlike conventional house arrest systems that simply note when an offender leaves or returns home, the SMART bracelet contains built-in rules of release which dictate exactly where the wearer should be at all times.

When the poor S.O.B. goes anywhere outside the dotted lines he gets a warning and then the system dials up the great central monitor in the sky and snitches the guy off.

SMART also sends out GPS locations on pre-determined basis showing the actual location of any given offender on a PC based map display down at the department of corrections. Not only can officers monitor parolees exact movements, a database can be created, stored on a web site, and the target's overall rehabilitation can be accessed as well a providing info for criminal investigations.

NSR's *SkyTracker*™ enables users to track high value assets and relay critical information via the ORBCOMM satellite network. Whether you need to track hazardous materials, highly mobile assets, contraband, or personnel, *SkyTracker* is a cost-effective, reliable messaging and locating system. *SkyTracker* collects critical position and attribute data from mobile assets and routes it, via the ORBCOMM network, for client access via e-mail, Internet, or dial-up.

NSR is currently developing state-of-the-art asset tracking and reporting capabilities for law enforcement applications for the U.S. Army and the National Institute of Justice. These applications include both covert and overt methods of collecting critical information.

NSR offers ORBCOMM network access and *SkyTracker* services for a complete range of remote two-way data communications applications:

**National Systems & Research Co.,** 5475 Mark Dabling Blvd. Suite 200, Colorado Springs, CO 80918 www.nsr.com. Very slick, reasonably priced GPS locating and communication products.

Used by many commercial trucking companies as well as the Justice Department NSR systems are designed to be used with existing communication systems as well as cellular carriers.

They offer a variety of units as well as a service which provides central tracking with call-in or automatic position updating.

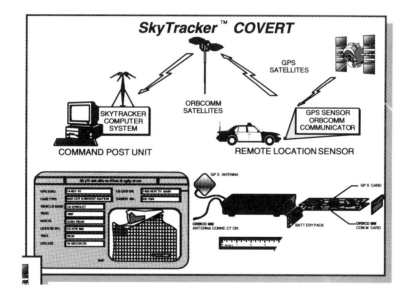

---

**Tracking**, tracking, tracking. Consumers beware! While Japan offers a service that will track "your wife" via her cell phone and provide a printed daily report of her movements and stops, California has just now made it illegal to place a tracking device on anyone's auto (LE excepted, of course).

---

**Trimble Navigation Limited** 645 North Mary Ave., POB 3642 Sunnyvale, CA 94088 www.trimble.com. Probably the world's largest and most sophisticated OEM of industrial GPS tracking systems they have *just* released the most inexpensive covert type GPS system ever offered.

Already appearing in other people's catalogs for much more money.

The Placer GPS 400 receiver is a low-cost, high-performance GPS receiver that provides accurate vehicle position, velocity, and time in all weather conditions. The receiver has six channels which track up to eight satellites in order to automatically determine the optimum satellite combination and calculate the best possible position solution. For applications requiring enhanced position accuracy, differential-ready versions of the Placer GPS 400 process RTCM differential GPS corrections for up to 2- to 5-meter accuracy.

The Placer GPS 400 features a "two-piece" configuration that protects it against vandalism and other types of damage. The receiver is housed inside the vehicle while the unobtrusive low-profile antenna is mounted outside the vehicle. This configuration allows discrete use of positioning technology for sensitive applications.

The Placer GPS 400 receiver integrates easily with Trimble's vehicle tracking systems. A standard RS-232 serial interface outputs vehicle location in Trimble ASCII Interface Protocol (TAIP) using characters compatible with personal computers, laptops, mobile data terminals, modems, and data radios.

Once installed, the Placer GPS 400 receiver requires no user intervention during either power up or normal operation. Users program the system to send position reports at specified time or distance intervals based on epoch and frequency or distance traveled. These features prevent network congestion and protect dispatchers against receiving redundant reports from idle or low-activity vehicles.

With Trimble's optional GPS Starter Kit (GPSSK) software, the user can connect to a DOS-based computer and communicate with the receiver right out of the box. With GPSSK, users can send and receive Placer GPS 400 messages, plot vehicle locations in real time on a computer screen, and configure their units for specific applications.

The Placer GPS 400 belongs to Trimble's line of Placer vehicle location receivers. This product line includes the Placer GPS 400, standard and inverted differential variants, and integrated high-performance GPS/dead reckoning units. The Placer GPS 400 supports transparent modems and DATARADIO's DMP™ protocol. All Placer receivers use the identical TAIP protocol so that users can select the right mix of Placer receivers to meet their application needs. Easy-to-use and install, the Placer GPS 400 is the ideal receiver for fleet managers, system integrators, and OEM suppliers.

**Paradigm Advanced Technologies** 1 Concord Globe #201 Don Mills, Ont. M3C 3NG The Guardian Angel R-2 is a personal security device that enables instant transmission of the targets' longitude and latitude location to someone concerned about such matters. This simple, battery operated, lightweight unit can be concealed on a person, worn on a belt or carried in a hand or purse.

Paradigm states the unit is small enough to stash on a person or a package.

The PinPoint Tracking System utilizes a seamless map of the entire United States. The vehicle you are tracking is represented on the computer screen as either a dot or an arrow. The dot is present when the vehicle is stationary, the arrow is present when the vehicle is in motion and points in the direction of travel. The "bread crumb" feature will leave a trail of dots and arrows showing the vehicles activity. The map also provides on screen monitoring of the vehicles speed, altitude, direction of travel in degrees, and the time and date of the activity. You can save the tracking session to a file and recall the vehicles activity when needed. You may want to include the tracking session in a report or as an exhibit, for this you have the option to export as a bitmap or windows metafile image. The map also has drawing and labeling features. If you find a new street or a subdivision that's too new to be on the map, you can add it so your system is always up to date.

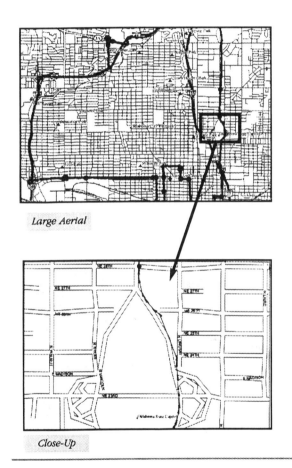

*Large Aerial*

*Close-Up*

**Pinpoint Tracking** 15 N. Robinson, Suite 1200, Oklahoma City, OK 73102. OEM of covert GPS systems designed specifically for investigators.

**DTI Surveillance Products**, Direction Technology, Inc., POB 911, Centreville, VA 20122 www.directionfinder.com. Can't think of too much to add to this listing.

**Delorme** Two Delorme Drive, Yarmouth, ME 04096 www.delorme.com. OEM of mapping software including Street Atlas USA. Used by many GPS locating and tracking products.

Also very low cost hardware; not designed for covert use but may have applications...

# DeLorme Product List

## A comprehensive Line of Mapping Software and Navigation Products

**AAA Map'n'Go® 4.0** — *The smart way to plan a trip, anywhere in North America!*

- New user-friendly interface
- 1998 AAA database of over 64,000 accommodations, restaurants, campgrounds and points of interest
- GPS voice navigation allows AAA Map'n'Go to "talk" to users when traveling with a GPS receiver
- Slide show enables users to insert photos into travelogue and play it or e-mail it

- TripPix allows users to place photos on the map
- Links to Internet for weather and road construction updates and event information (**www.mapngo.com**)
- 3Com® PalmPilot™ support allows users to send route directions and AAA TourBook information to a PalmPilot

*Estimated Street Price $39.00*

**Street Atlas USA® 5.0** — *Detailed street level maps of the entire USA and much, much more*

- New address-to-address routing
- Symbols on the maps show location and phone numbers of over 2 million businesses and other points of interest
- GPS voice navigation enables users to "hear" directions when traveling with a GPS receiver

- Comprehensive listings of services available at Interstate exits
- Direct Internet access to hundreds of city Web pages for detailed regional information
- PalmPilot ready

*Estimated Street Price $45.00*

**DeLorme Tripmate™ GPS Receiver** — *Always know exactly where you are!*

- An easy-to-use connection to the Global Positioning System(GPS)Lowest-priced, high performance GPS receiver available

- Displays moving or stationary position on Street Atlas USA 5.0 or AAA Map'n'Go 4.0 maps

*Estimated Street Price $159.00*

**Simply Streets USA™** — *A detailed street map of the entire country, at a low price*

**Tactical Technologies** 1701 Second Ave Folsom PA 19033. The Shadow starts with a passive box, stores 32,000 readings one can download. Works with IBM computer and good US mapping software. Can then add dial-in modem, real time GPS and so on for real time tracking.

Fairly expensive.

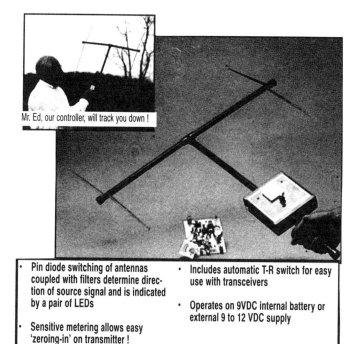

Mr. Ed, our controller, will track you down !

- Pin diode switching of antennas coupled with filters determine direction of source signal and is indicated by a pair of LEDs

- Sensitive metering allows easy 'zeroing-in' on transmitter !

- Includes automatic T-R switch for easy use with transceivers

- Operates on 9VDC internal battery or external 9 to 12 VDC supply

**Ramsey Electronics, Inc.**, 793 Canning Parkway, Victor, NY 14564 www.ramseyelectronics.com. A very inexpensive, unique two antenna signal tracking system for transmitter locating.

**Corp Ten International** POB 20177 Baltimore, MD 21284. Autofind automatic vehicle, vessel and aircraft tracking configured in a variety of formats from "carry and go" mobile units to permanent installs.

Utilizing a 2" patch antenna and radio/cellular/satellite communications this system is ideal for covert tracking.

## System Operation:

The **AUTOFIND** system can be easily installed in a variety of assets desired to be tracked. The mobile unit (VDML) installed in the vehicle includes a GPS receiver and a two inch patch antenna that receives the GPS satellite signals and calculates its own position. The vehicle position and other information is then transmitted – depending on the mobile unit used — via radio, trunking, cellular telephone or digital satellite to the base station. The base station receiver unit processes the signal from the mobile unit and displays the vehicle on a computer digital map along with other information such as speed, heading, alarm status, siren, door open/shut and any additional data. The data that is displayed for the vehicles can be customized for each user.

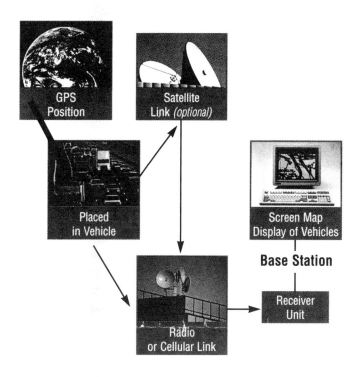

GPS Position

Satellite Link *(optional)*

Placed in Vehicle

Screen Map Display of Vehicles

**Base Station**

Radio or Cellular Link

Receiver Unit

# COMPUTER SURVEILLANCE
## And Attack

**Total Recall Corporation** 50A South Main Street, Spring Valley, NY 10977 www.Totalrecallcorp.com. besides their quite complete catalog of covert video equipment TRC also offers a phone wire based video transmission system.

## VIDEO PHONE TRANSMISSION

With today's technology, it is possible to view your CCTV system from a remote location. Video phone transmission systems give you the ability to be off-site and spot check activity. You can now view your convenience store, pharmacy, check cashing operation, car wash or any business and even your house from a remote location! Monitor store openings and closings, spot check activity during the day (Is the store busy? Are deliveries received properly? Are unauthorized people in your store?) Total Recall sells many different video phone transmission systems. They range from simple systems that operate using the phone keypad to PC based systems. TRC is an authorized dealer for: Telesite, Robot and Dedicated Micros. Call one of our application specialists to find out more about video phone transmission systems and how they can help you and your business.

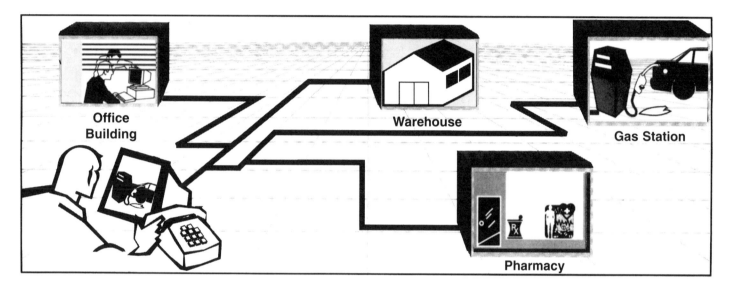

**8x8 Inc.,** 2445 Mission College Blvd., Santa Clara, CA. 95045 www.8x8.com. A black box about the size and shape of a video cassette tape hooks up to the surveillance camera(s) of your choice and then to a standard touch tone telephone.

Operator, who owns second black box (actually called the RSM-1500) which is hooked up a TV monitor and/or VCR dials in and see and hears all that be happeni' in full color, on real time.

Unit is portable so can be keyed for a variety of remote sites.

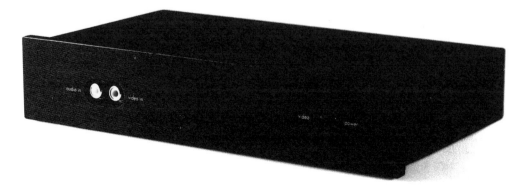

**Prescient Systems** 1259 El Camino Real #200, Menlo Park, CA 94025 www.gotchanow.com one of the best low priced video capture PC based software. Gotcha! Personal Observation Software defaults to motion detection recording but has a number of varying variables that enhance this low priced system.

Check 'em out.

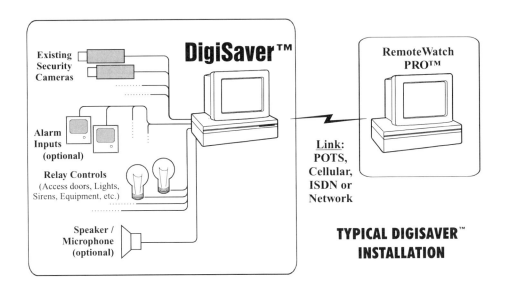

**TeleSite USA** 45 Central Avenue Tenafly, NJ 07670 www.telesiteusa.com. Upscale full color phone line video transmission system . Great reputation for quality products.

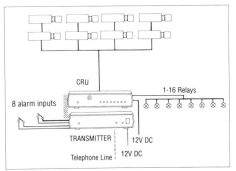

Single CRU Layout (Transmitter Site Only)

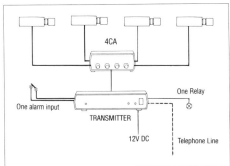

4CA Layout (Transmitter Site Only)

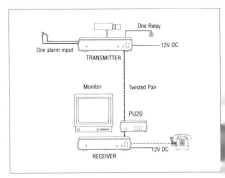

PU20

**Alpha Systems Lab** 17712 Mitchell North, Irvine, CA 92614 www.aslrp.com. A professional, medium level remote video tele-surveillance and recording system. Flexible as to means of transmission as well as digital storage of video or stills on any hard drive.

## TYPICAL RemoteWatch™ PRO SYSTEM LAYOUT

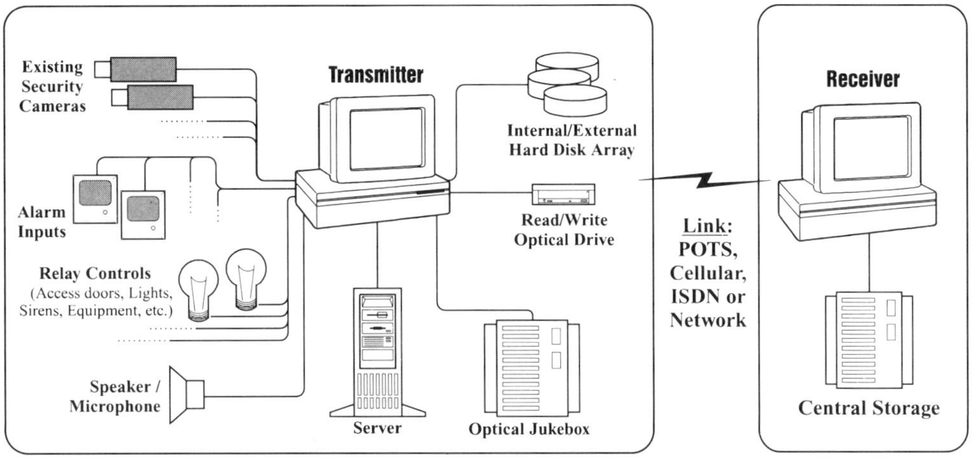

# TeleEye Pro - World's Fastest Phone Line CCTV System

**Signal Communications LTD.**, 217, 2F., Hong Kong Industrial Technology Centre, Fat Chee Ave. Kowloon, Hong King www.TeleEye.com. Buy directly from this OEM of a fast digital transmission which can handle 16 cameras; accepts various different triggering options including dial up activation.

- Alarm triggering
- Multi Site Monitoring
- LAN and Internet access
- Various transmission types
- Programmable recording

**Darim Vision Co.**, LTD., 3460 Wilshire Blvd, Suite #1114, Los Angeles, CA 90010 www.darvision.com. A number of remote surveillance products including the PC Snoop series which provides three levels of security. In the stealth mode the software, tethered to a tiny digital camera records all motion within range on the hard disc stopping when the action stops, starting when the action resumes. Date, time and duration also "stamped" onto hard disc.

Watchdog mode records but also sounds an alarm (default is a "barking dog") to subtly suggest intruder move along.

Digital Secretary records and then produces an audio message (something to the effect of "thanks for dropping by, don't steal anything, leave a nice video message.")

Also offer a remote digital video surveillance system that lets one dial up and view real time (compressed) video on one's PC. Or the "Tiny Guardian" will dial up the PC when it senses motion.

Will automatically record decoded video on hard drive for later examination.

*[handwritten margin note: You can copy the footage on hard disk to a CD DVD using a CD DVD rewriter (AKA "CD writer", "CDRW")]*

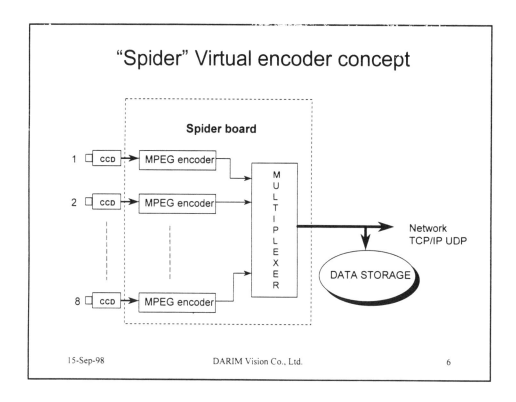

"Spider" Virtual encoder concept

Spider board

1 CCD → MPEG encoder
2 CCD → MPEG encoder
8 CCD → MPEG encoder

MULTIPLEXER → Network TCP/IP UDP

DATA STORAGE

15-Sep-98    DARIM Vision Co., Ltd.    6

**Tech Assist, Inc.**, 11350 66 Street., Ste. 105, Largo, FL 33773 www.toolsthatwork.com. Designers of a number of extremely useful computer programs.

Omniquad Desktop Surveillance enables one to monitor any computer's usage by actually taking snapshots of the computer screen at user defined intervals or when selected applications are started.

These images are stored for later playback on the machine itself or kept at a remote site. The program can also send the files, automatically, via email to any other computer on the net.

Also a facility for real time surveillance. Shareware, free trial, very inexpensive to keep.

Also a couple of other necessary programs as follows...

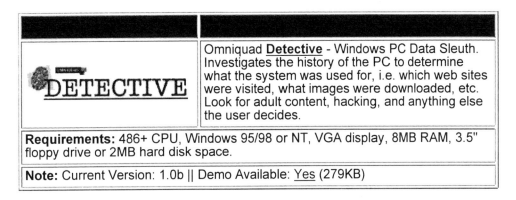

Omniquad **Detective** - Windows PC Data Sleuth. Investigates the history of the PC to determine what the system was used for, i.e. which web sites were visited, what images were downloaded, etc. Look for adult content, hacking, and anything else the user decides.

**Requirements:** 486+ CPU, Windows 95/98 or NT, VGA display, 8MB RAM, 3.5" floppy drive or 2MB hard disk space.

**Note:** Current Version: 1.0b || Demo Available: <u>Yes</u> (279KB)

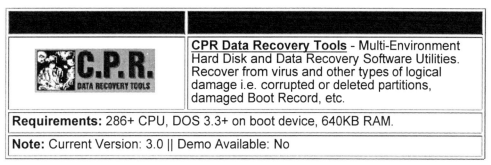

**CPR Data Recovery Tools** - Multi-Environment Hard Disk and Data Recovery Software Utilities. Recover from virus and other types of logical damage i.e. corrupted or deleted partitions, damaged Boot Record, etc.

**Requirements:** 286+ CPU, DOS 3.3+ on boot device, 640KB RAM.

**Note:** Current Version: 3.0 || Demo Available: No

**Berryhill Computer Forensics** POB 1674 Benicia, CA 94510 www.computerforensics.com. A specialized firm for data recovery and analysis with the emphasis on trial evidence preparation.

### Search and Seizure Services

Training in search and seizure procedures.
Consultation on search warrant preparation.
Assistance on site with search and seizure of computers.

### Preservation and Analysis Services

Exact image copies of hard drives, floppy disks and other media.
Password cracking.
Keyword searches.
Document and financial data extraction.
Recovery of accidentally or intentionally deleted data.

**Primary Image Ltd.**, POB 781207 Orlando, FL 32878. High end video motion detector that studies )"memorizes" a scene and automatically starts recording if anything moves.

Also very slick, expensive, fully digital recording system.

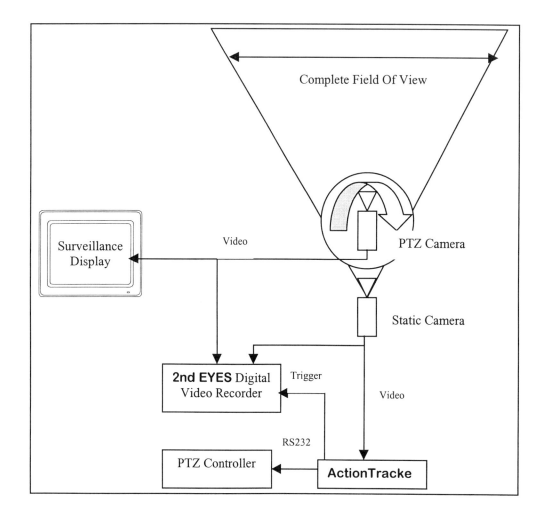

**OzVision Ltd.**, K. Nahal Oz D.N. Negev 85145 Israel. OzCam a integrated camera with an optical sensor, digital compressor and high speed modem. Unit will transmit high quality b and w video over telephone lines to any PC equipped with their proprietary software.

Software will decompress and display live video, record digital video on a hard disc as well as replay and enhance saved video.

OzCam can be programmed to call out when motion is detected.

**GYYR** (available only thru dealers) Just introduced the Multilink Remote Monitoring Communication System, a turnkey program for remote monitoring of multiple VCR's via the phone line.

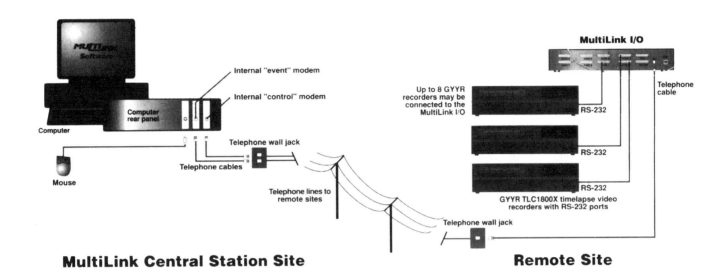

**MultiLink Central Station Site**　　　　**Remote Site**

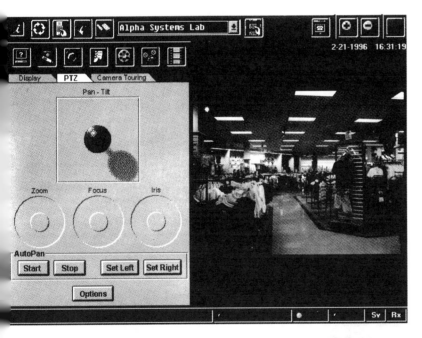

## Remote Video Management

- Site touring and camera touring continuously or as needed for Remote Video Surveillance, Guard Tour and Alarm Verification.
- Site touring saves manpower, improves safety, shortens response time, increases peace of mind.

## Remote Video Access Control

- Full remote control of inputs (intrusion and motion sensors, panic, etc.) and outputs (siren, lights, etc.).
- Remote personnel identification/verification.
- Remote entry/exit control into and out of secured areas.

## Remote Camera Control

- Remotely activate Pan, Tilt & Zoom camera controls and presets.

# REMOTEWATCH™PRO
# gives you long-distance eyes & ears!

**CCS** 360 Madison Ave., New York, NY 10017 www.spyzone.com CCS's entry into the remote video observation field. Cute, expensive.

**ACTUAL SIZE OF LENS IS ONLY 5/16" DIAMETER... LENS CAN BE EASILY HIDDEN IN ANY HOUSING SUCH AS:**

a clock radio or other household device

# Global Watch

## Command Center & Video System

**SPYCAM-11 COMMUNICATES DIRECTLY THROUGH PHONE LINES TO YOUR PC OR LAPTOP**

a cash register, file cabinet or any store fixture

It will install in a yacht, summer house, warehouse, home, garage, in the kid's room, kitchen...you name it.

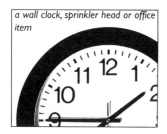

a wall clock, sprinkler head or office item

**Group Sense Limited** 27F., Wu Chung House, 213 Queen's Road East, Wanchai Hong Kong. SD-300X Instant View video surveillance system detects movement from any CCD camera and then transmits the data over standard phone lines to any 486 PC computer.

US distributor IPSS 12555 W. Jefferson Blvd., Suite 300, Los Angeles, CA 90066.

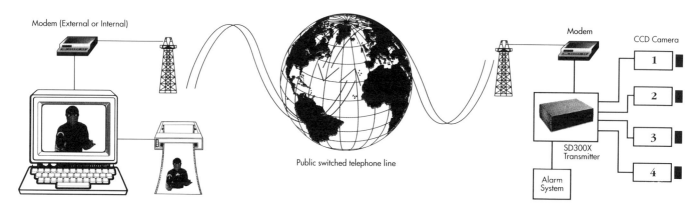

Modem (External or Internal)

Public switched telephone line

Modem

CCD Camera

1

2

3

4

SD300X Transmitter

Alarm System

Rampant capitalism has come to the hacking/cracking world! Take a hypothetical situation, fer instance, you have typed some really sensitive data on a particular computer or disc and some careless son-of-a-bitch, perhaps your maid, tosses out the only copy of your password with the six month old dog food can you had it carefully noted on.

Your only copy.

Now, of course, knowing my readers I realize none of you would consider using this procedure on someone else's programs that so I have no second thoughts about passing on a new company of now-legit hackers called **Crak Software**, whose very motto is "You Hack 'em, we Crack'em".

According to John Kuslich ("head geek what's in charge") Crak will recover lost passwords so you can access your data on damn near every word processor and spreadsheet program around...

So if you've got this encrypted file that is just screaming for a clear read?

Fax Crak at 602-548-1993 or visit their site at www.crak.com where you can down load sample (demo) programs and then give them a call for the security code to enable the software.

Victims, ah, rather potential targets include files encrypted in Word, Excel, Lotus, QuattroPro, WordPerfect, Quicken, Corel, Windows 95/NT, and so on.

In fact, Crak is so mainstream many of the tech support groups at the program providers (such as Microsoft) actually recommend Crak when frenzied customers demand they "find" the lost password to an important file.

Crak will not break heavy, government type NSA programs but will provide key escrowed encryption breaks (because the key itself is stored somewhere in the file).

Cost? under $200 for the latest WordPerfect security break, they take most major credit cards and will Fed Ex for those really urgent projects.

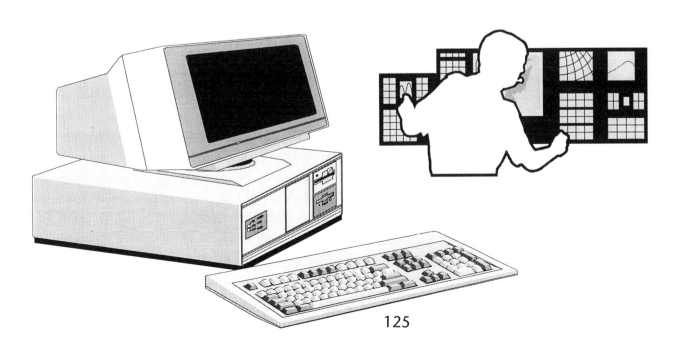

# CELL PHONES
## Interception And Blocking

**Aztec Research LLC.** 23352 Peralta, Suite 14, Laguna Hills, CA 92653. The CA1000 series of cellular analyzers are quite slick and offer almost everything one would ask Santa (or Buddha, whatever) for in the way of a cellular tracker/monitor.

This particular unit is a handheld unit that fits in your shirt pocket but extremely powerful with regard to features and applications.

Fer instance – The basic unit, called the **LE** is available for purchase by both legal eagles and PI's, the difference being that the PI/private version has the audio section blocked by a proprietary password.

The LE can still be legally employed in a number of important tactical situations *without* the audio and then if lightening strikes and the user receives a legal warrant, it can be "unblocked" when said user presents "appropriate documentation".

The above board, legal for you and me unit will still do a number of remarkable things. To whit:

- Monitor cellular usage (no audio), keep a record of any calls dialed from that particular phone and then *track it down* for you…

- Once a legit wiretap warrant is issued the unit will allow for direct monitoring, logging and recording of cellular calls

- A "Geiger counter" signal strength meter (with audio) coupled with a yagi (directional) antenna pistol grip will track down and particular phone within a *few feet* of its location

Typically the LE (with antenna) would be used to locate a phone within a specific building, then eliminate each floor until the strongest signal appears and then the HTGAOA reader would progress to specific rooms.

Besides the law enforcement and "authorized civvie" versions a Cell Shop CA1000 is available as a fool proof reader, ESN recorder and phone identifier. The **CS1000** monitors 8 reverse control channels simultaneously, allows reads form any phone regardless of carrier selection, highlights fraudulent ESN and errant mobile number ID.

## *JIUNAN-01 Cellular Phone Monitoring System*

- **System includes:**
    - WWCIA-438M cellular phone interceptor
    - WWCIA-439M cellular phone interceptor (calculator cover)
    - ER-228 cellular phone ESN reader
- **WWCIA-438M Cellular Phone Interceptor**
    1. Works in either AMPS or ETACS systems
    2. Monitors either cellular system A or B
    3. Operates both in general monitoring or targets specific phone by number
    4. Identifies unknown cellular mobile phone number
    5. Identifies the active channel by number
    6. Cell site specific monitoring mode setting available
    7. Decode touch tones used to access voice mail, answering machines, etc
    8. Targets 20 mobile numbers for all calls made in or out
    9. Automatically records both sides of all conversations as connected with voice control recorder
    10. Tracks hand-offs from cell to cell when following vehicle
    11. Time setting and DTMF output enable
    12. Can be used as normal cellular phone
    13. Power: DC 6V
    14. Dmensions: 170 x 55 x 30mm
    15. Weight: 350g (not including battery & antenna)

**Jiun An Technology Co., Ltd.**, 1F No. 12, Shao Hsing St., Taipei, Taiwan www.asiansources.com/jiunan.co. Jiun Also offers a fairly low priced cellular monitor that works on all present systems (except digital, of course).

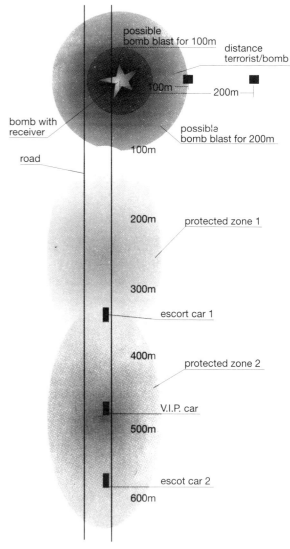

**HP Marketing** Wust GMBH Grootkoppel 9, 23858 Reinfield. For those of you not happy with just blanking out cell phones this company makes a jammer that blocks all radio signals for a range of several hundred meters. Designed for remote bomb protection the uses are endless.

## No Cell Phone

Recently two different companies have introduced cell phone blockers. Both these units will effectively shut down all cell phone communications within a given radius from the unit.

The first is known as WaveWall and is available from a Japanese firm called **Medic**. Much like Tylenol the basic system comes in two different strengths. The normal (known as the "Fairy", I kid you not) version will not let any phone transmit or receive within a 20 foot radius of the cigarette pack sized transmitter.

The "Hyper30" is 1,000 times as powerful (about a 30 meter knockout zone).

Why would anyone want such a device?

According to Medic –

"Japanese people's manners have gone from bad to worse. Our product compensate for this with technology," – Kyoin Takafuji, director of Medic Inc.

The unit retails for $480 and can be ordered by visiting their web page at:

www.medic.co.jp/products/wavewall

Although I will warn you the site is in Japanese...

Stay with the buttons and you can get an English translation as well as an email order form.

**Special Electronic Security Products, Ltd.**, 12/B Rahavat-Ilan Street, POB 19 Givat-Shmuel, 54056 Israel www.sesp.co.il provides a second Cell phone stopper that has been around for a while, at least in the military arena from a company in Israel – "Cellular Telephone Immobilizer Model: SPY-456 is a Jamming System designed to paralyze and immobilize the 2-way full-duplex RF-links between mobile cellular telephones and the stationary cellular cells with which they are communicating. All mobile telephones within the predetermined area in which the system has been installed will lose their 2-way RF-link with the cells, and become completely neutralized and unable to transmit or receive any calls. When immobilized, the cellular telephones will display a 'NO SERVICE' message. Product Specification, SPY-456 Model:

Effective at ALL cellular systems, analogue and digital (CDMA, GSM and others). Power Output: Adjustable between 10 mW to 1000 mW. Range of Coverage: The effective radius of operation can be adjusted between 2 to 200 meters. The range is controlled by the power output. Antenna: Omnidirectional, 50 ohm. Modulation: Compound (Patent pending). Frequency Coverage Range: 880 - 920 Mhz. Power source: 110V or 220V. Backup Battery: Up to 12 hours of operation. Dimensions: 250 x 200 x 70 mm (without antenna). Case: Metal. Installed in an attaché case, complete with battery.Can be camouflaged inside ordinary looking radio or TV sets, etc."

# PARALYSER AND NEUTRALIZER
## OF CELLULAR TELEPHONES.

### DESCRIPTION.
ALL CELLULAR TELEPHONES WITHIN A RADIUS OF UP TO 100 METERS* FROM THE "CTN-100" WILL BE TOTALLY PARALYSED, RENDERED INOPERABLE, AND THUS UNABLE TO TRANSMIT OR RECEIVE CALLS. THE "CTN-100" IS EASILY OPERATED BY SIMPLY SWITCHING IT "ON" OR "OFF". REMOTE CONTROL OPERATION IS OPTIONAL. POWERED BY EITHER AC 220/110 VOLTS OR A 12 VOLT CAR OR RECHARGEABLE BATTERY. *LONGER RANGES OPTIONAL. THE "CTN-100", BEING FULLY PORTABLE, CAN BE OPERATED IN VARIOUS LOCATIONS. THE SYSTEM CAN BE SUPPLIED INSTALLED IN AN ATTACHE CASE, COMPLETE WITH ITS BATTERY, OR, CAMOUFLAGED INSIDE AN ORDINARY RADIO OR TV ETC. (AS PER CUSTOMERS' REQUEST).

# OPTICS AND NIGHT VISION

**Litton Electro-Optical Systems** 3414 Herrmann Dr., Garland, TX 75041. Litton is one of the only (ITT and one other) OEM of image intensifier tubes in the US. They package their tubes in mil spec pocket scopes, goggles and weapon sights.

Whether you plan on flying your helicopter at night, shooting some SOB 400 yards distant in the dark of night or just want to see what you are missing, there is a Litton product designed for what you need.

Probably best to get the company catalog, check out what would work for you, compare dealer prices.

Besides it's a lot of fun read.

Kind of like Tom Clancy.

The LP/NVG is a unique patented folded-optical design that provides a stable, low center-of-gravity, self-contained goggle for multi-mission roles of parachuting; land / water / aircraft operation in both urban and field environments.

Its unique beam combiner design provides a direct vision path during transitions from low light conditions into brightly lighted environments. This see-through capability, which provides excellent peripheral vision, offers greater flexibility and situational awareness for helicopter, cargo, and attack aircraft crewmemebers. The LP/NVG's low profile permits freedom of movement in wooded or rough terrain.

LP/NVG is powered by 1/2 or 2/3 AA batteries. The image intensifires are turned on by a OFF/ON switch which is controlled separately from the built-in twin IR illuminators. They have their own OFF/ON/ON switch that allows the use of a two position low and high illumination settings.

LP/NVG is also compatible for injecting heads up display information into the field of view be it symbology, alphanumerics, or FLIR imagery. Integrated GPS navigation information is readily adaptable to the HUD data entry port.

LP/NVG can be supplied with either GEN II or GEN III tubes. Each monocular has an objective lens, an image intensifier assembly, eyepiece with HUD port input, and a beamcombiner. The beamcombiner folds the intensified image so that it enters the operator's eye laid on top of the scene which the operator sees directly through the beamcombiner. Circuits for the left and right monocular are independent so that a short in one will not stop operation of the other.

# 260/250
Generation 3    Generation 2

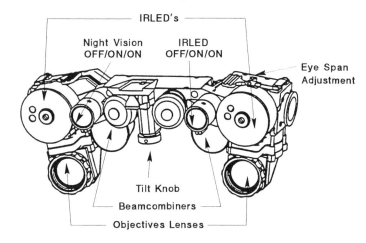

IRLED's

Night Vision OFF/ON/ON    IRLED OFF/ON/ON

Eye Span Adjustment

Tilt Knob
Beamcombiners
Objectives Lenses

A good source for optical gear is outdoor and sporting magazines. Bird watching magazines and newsletters, in particular carry various scopes, lenses and a very slick one-handed camera steadying device.

The latter unit lends itself to surveillance applications, and is, in fact sold by a number of spy shops.

# 160/150
Generation 3    Generation 2

**Canon U.S.A., Inc.,** One Canon Plaza, Lake Success, NY 11042. Outstanding optic OEM Cannon's new line includes a series of optically stabilized binoculars which allow higher powered, distortion free surveillance.

**Eliminated "image shake," which was a major problem with binoculars.**
**Uses the most advanced image stabilizer.**

Almost everybody who has ever used binoculars at sporting events or concerts has experienced how much the images shake, and you feel that the binoculars are useless. The main complaint of users has been image shake. The higher the magnification, the larger the image shake. In general, any binoculars with over 10x magnification should not be used for a long time. The best solution in the past was to use a tripod. However, tripods are bulky and can't be used everywhere. Even if you need a pair of binoculars of over 10x magnification for bird watching, the most you would want to use since you walk around a lot would be something of 7x or 8x magnification.

Canon is the world's first maker to use an active optical image stabilizer for IS series. Because two Vari-Angle Prisms are controlled by a microprocessor, hand shake is eliminated (Fig. 8). As a result, even with over 10x magnification, a tripod is not needed. And they can even be used while viewing from a moving car or train! In addition to the light weight, there is no eye strain to make you tired, so it is possible to use these binoculars for a long time.

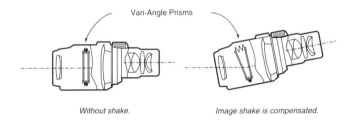

Vari-Angle Prisms

*Without shake.*　　　　*Image shake is compensated.*

Aquila III NVD (made by Litton). Even through we've covered Litton this brand new entry should get a look because of its versatility and rugged construction.

AN/PVS-12 is an individually served weaponsight. The standard model meets 1 meter submersion in water for 30 minutes. The AN/PVS-12A is an optional model that can be carried underwater unprotected to 66 feet. They are constructed from proven high strength aluminum alloy designed to survive rugged military environments. The surface finish is non-reflective matte black. AN/PVS-12 interfaces with a wide range of weapons by utilizing the M16, STANAG, or Weaver mounting base. Available adapters enable the sight to be mounted for user comfort. AN/PVS-12 low profile allows for an excellent cheek weld particularly on weapons with a flat rail design.

Controls and adjustments are simple to operate. Proper focus is maintained by turning an eyepiece ring. An ON / OFF knob controls reticle brightness. Zeroing is accomplished by correcting azimuth and elevation knobs. A daylight cover is attached to permit boresighting and training during the day or dawn & dusk time periods. A soft rubber eyeguard with a light security flap provides the marksman with operational safety.

AN/PVS-12 can be equipped with either GEN III or GEN II image intensifiers to meet customer requirements.

## MINI NIGHT VISION WEAPON SIGHT
### Aquila III

The Aquila III is an upgraded design of the Aquila I Mini weapon sight, and features a new family of objectives and an afocal which allows the use of one basic night vision system to be customized for a variety of individual and crew-served weapons. Aquila III is offered with either an 18mm GEN II or GEN III image intensifier. The objectives and afocal lenses are the same as with the new AN/PVS-10 for commonality of spare parts.

The system can be ordered as either 4X, 6X, or 4X with screw-on afocal to achieve 6X magnification. It is constructed of high strength aluminum to withstand the most rugged environments. Mounting for a wide range of weapons with common systems such as STANAG or Weaver is available, as are custom mounts. The system operates on two "AA" batteries.

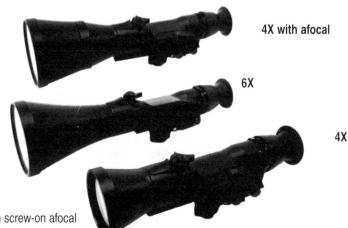

4X with afocal

6X

4X

**North American Integrated Technologies** POB 82049 San Diego, CA 92138. NAIT has been one of the best OEM night vision suppliers in the US. Intelligence Incorporated has carried (and used) NAIT equipment including their monocular pocket scope and been very happy with the results.

Units are constructed with aircraft aluminum bodies, interchangeable front and back lenses and first quality tubes.

Recently NAIT has combined with La France Specialties initiating a joint operation dedicated to the night vision and combat weapon/silencer market.

Look into NAIT's selections before purchasing either night vision or silencers.

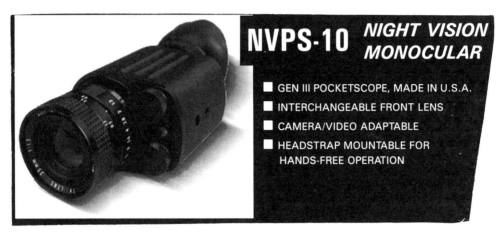

**NVPS-10** *NIGHT VISION MONOCULAR*

- GEN III POCKETSCOPE, MADE IN U.S.A.
- INTERCHANGEABLE FRONT LENS
- CAMERA/VIDEO ADAPTABLE
- HEADSTRAP MOUNTABLE FOR HANDS-FREE OPERATION

**Inframetrics** 16 Esquire Rd., North Bilerica, MA 01862. Very slick, high end OEM supplier of thermal imaging systems for the military, law enforcement, aerospace, and industrial uses.

**MilCAM,®** a hardened miniature infrared camera for military thermal imaging applications, provides high-resolution thermal images in total darkness, degraded environmental conditions, and through most battlefield obscurants. The unit may be used for surveillance, commander's viewer, battle damage assessment, and target marking applications. Weighing just three pounds (1.4 kg) with 8.8° FOV lens and battery. MilCAM offers tremendous reliability through an elegant, simplistic, modular design. Single FOV, dual FOV, continuous zoom, and dual band interchangeable lenses are offered for short-, medium-, and long-range viewing and targeting applications.

*MilCAM*™

134

**After Dark Products Co.,** POB 1680 Berthoud, CO 80513. Reseller of ITT, Texas Instruments, Litton night scopes and thermal imagers. Add in a couple of Russian units with IR laser enhancement (see photo), camera adapters, good prices and an interesting sales policy ("many of our customers only have a first name and we don't care") and ADP becomes a useful source.

*Limited time ONLY*

**$399.00**
*for 5.5X add $50.00*

| "White Night" model 323 Technical Data | | |
|---|---|---|
| Distance of Visibility: "Starlight" | 400 yards | 450 yards |
|     "Quarter Moon" | 500 yards | 550 yards |
|     "Total Darkness" | 150 yards | 175 yards |
| Visual magnification | 3.5X | 5.5X |
| Resolution | 38 lp/mm | 38 lp/mm |
| Dimensions | 7.5 X 2.5 X 3.75" | 8.5 X 2.5 X 3.75" |
| Weight | 1.6 lb | 1.8 lb |
| Price | $449.00 | $489.00 |

**Search Systems** POB 80307 Bakersfield, CA 93380. Video cameras mounted on a variety of probes for a variety of purposes including searching for disaster victims to searching for enemies. Most models include audio and either visible or IR lighting. Professional, expensive systems.

**Electrophysics** 373 Route 46 West, Bldg. E, Fairfield, NJ 07004 wwwelectrophysicscorp.com. OEM of an in-between camera intensifier. The EP unit (9350) is designed to fit in-between a camera body and its lens. This idea allows one unit to be used on virtually every camera around from Nikon F-types to a variety of camcorders.

Besides the option to move the unit from camera to camera this concept allows for quick and easy front lens replacement.

## An optimum configuration for every camera

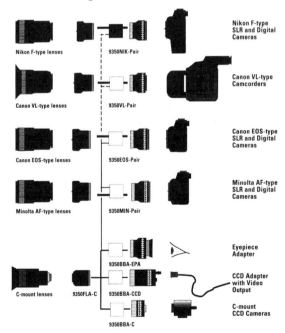

## Turn Darkness into Light

The 9350 extends the camera's usable light range without the drawbacks of slower shutter speeds or time integration.

**Raytheon TI Systems** POB 17151, Denver, CO 80217. The lowest cost, handheld near IR vision system as we go to press (left). **Alpec** 201 Richenbacker, Pl., Livermore, CA 94550 www.alpec.com (right) laser sights, pointers, pasters, laser enhanced shooting glasses.  Etc....

RTIS' New Portable Unit–The PalmIR 250

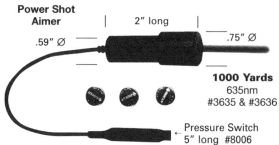

Power Shot Aimer

.59" Ø    2" long    .75" Ø

**1000 Yards**
635nm
#3635 & #3636

← Pressure Switch
5" long #8006

*The **Power Shot** is extremely compact and bright. These laser sights feature a mounting system that allows shooters to install mounts on all their firearms and quickly transfer the **Power Shot** from one to another.*

**B.E. Meyers & Co.,** 17525 NE 67th Court, Redmond, WA 98052 www.bemeyers.com. OEM of Dark Invader and Owl night vision gear they have expanded their line to include some pinhole and surveillance cameras, laser illuminators, and so on.

Very large selection (400 different NVD to camera adapters alone) of very well respected gear.

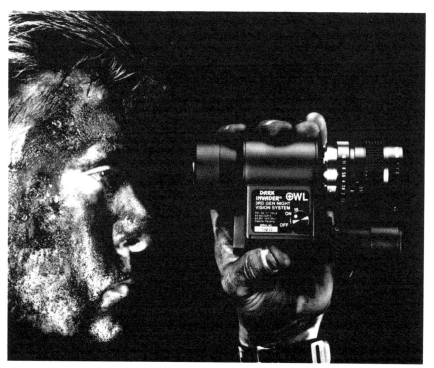

# SUPER 3RD GENERATION

### DARK INVADER® "OWL®" SUPER 3RD GENERATION+ MULTI-PURPOSE POCKETSCOPE#7000-I/S.

This unit is identical to the #7000-I DARK INVADER® "OWL®" with the exception it utilizes a new SUPER high output (OMNI 4) image intensifier tube. This advanced intensifier system will produce a light gain from 45,000-65,000 times, mil. spec. is normally 25,000 times. Image resolution is increased to 64 lp/mm or more as compared to mil. spec. at 36 lp/mm. The tube's photocathode sensitivity (ability to see in ultra low light) is a whopping 1800-2000 microamps/lumen as compared to 1000 microamps/lumen for mil. spec.

This SUPER DARK INVADER® "OWL®" will provide brighter images with much more definition in both the visible and near infrared  wave lengths.

**Nightline, Inc**. POB 16-0819 Miami, FL 33116. Featuring Litton image intensifiers Nightline offers one of the most complete catalogs of handheld, weapon oriented, and special use NVD's available.

Good prices along with some very unique products (periscope sights for your tank or Howitzer). Also Maxa Beam portable searchlights and various IR marking devices.

**Excalibur Enterprises** POB 400, Fogelsville, PA 18051. Long time reseller of top American made night vision gear (most Litton tube based). They also make some of their own units as well as repair most other scopes for a reasonable fee.

Most units military spec (in fact, many are sold to the military. Good company, solid reputation for service and sales.

**Optical Systems Technology, Inc.,** 110 Kountz Lane, Freeport, PA 16229. Resellers on Star Tron (one of the original night vision pioneers) MK-880 pocketscope. This versatile unit is designed to be converted into a variety of configurations from weapons sights to camera units with the use of inexpensive adapters.

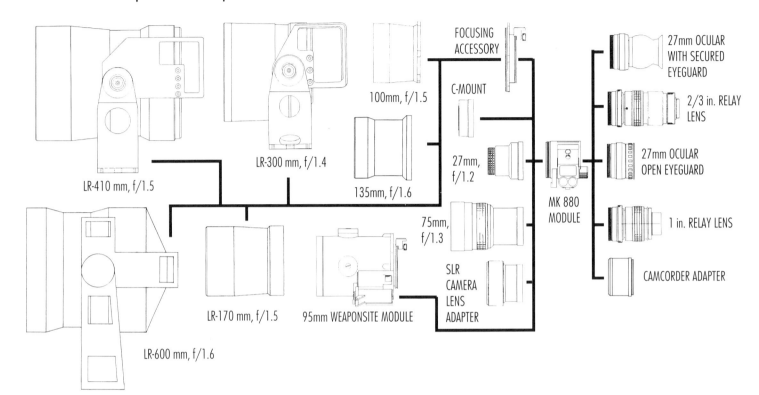

LR-410 mm, f/1.5
LR-300 mm, f/1.4
100mm, f/1.5
135mm, f/1.6
27mm, f/1.2
75mm, f/1.3
LR-170 mm, f/1.5
95mm WEAPONSITE MODULE
SLR CAMERA LENS ADAPTER
MK 880 MODULE
LR-600 mm, f/1.6
FOCUSING ACCESSORY
C-MOUNT
27mm OCULAR WITH SECURED EYEGUARD
2/3 in. RELAY LENS
27mm OCULAR OPEN EYEGUARD
1 in. RELAY LENS
CAMCORDER ADAPTER

**Optics** 411 Waverley Oaks Rd., Suite 144, Waltham, MA 02154. High end thermal imaging for industrial, military and law enforcement applications. The IR Cam is a palm sized thermal video camera **ION** that provides composite video output with no cryogenic cooling required.

## Helmet Mounted Camera

Ion Optics developed a special version of the Microcam Infrared Camera for mounting on a helmet. The miniature low power IR Microcam is well suited to helmet mounts, eliminating neck strain and heavy power packs. The system was incorporated with a visor viewer and processor to locate land mines through their IR signature. Other applications include fire fighting, night vision, search, and rescue.

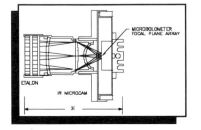

## Hypercam

Hyperspectral imaging, the ability to gather and process infrared spectral information from each pixel of an image, can ultimately provide two-dimensional chemical composition maps of a scene under study. Hypercam combines the IR camera with an electronically tunable etalon filter for hyperspectral imaging.

**Felix Security Devices**
POB 446 Oregon City, OR 97045. Felix is one of the best known suppliers of complete law enforcement surveillance vans. They also offer a high powered IR strobe and now carry some Russian NVD's.

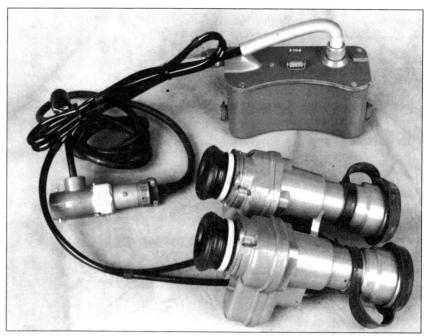

MPN 15K

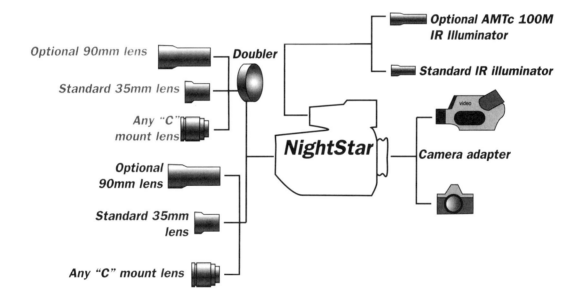

Optional 90mm lens — Doubler

Standard 35mm lens

Any "C" mount lens

Optional AMTc 100M IR Illuminator

Standard IR illuminator

Optional 90mm lens

Standard 35mm lens

Any "C" mount lens

*NightStar*

Camera adapter

video

**American Technologies Network Corp.,** 20 S. Linen Ave., South San Francisco, CA 94980. Provider of low end (1st, some 2nd generation) night vision scopes designed for easy conversation to camera lenses, binoculars and rifle scopes. Lens doublers, proximity detectors that turn the unit on and off automatically, along with some other neat stuff put ATNC a step above many other low end scopes.

**Cincinnati Electronics Corp.**, 7500 Innovation Way, Mason, OH 45040. A fairly recent entry in the all-electronic thermal imaging field.

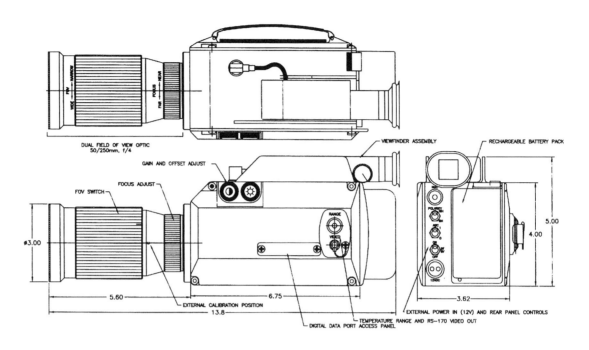

DUAL FIELD OF VIEW OPTIC
50/250mm, f/4

GAIN AND OFFSET ADJUST

FOCUS ADJUST

FOV SWITCH

Ø3.00

5.60

6.75

13.8

EXTERNAL CALIBRATION POSITION

DIGITAL DATA PORT ACCESS PANEL

TEMPERATURE RANGE AND RS–170 VIDEO OUT

RANGE

VIDEO

VIEWFINDER ASSEMBLY

RECHARGEABLE BATTERY PACK

5.00

4.00

3.62

EXTERNAL POWER IN (12V) AND REAR PANEL CONTROLS

**Nightline, Inc**. POB 16-0819 Miami, FL 33116. Featuring Litton image intensifiers Nightline offers one of the most complete catalogs of handheld, weapon oriented, and special use NVD's available.

Good prices along with some very unique products (periscope sights for your tank or Howitzer). Also Maxa Beam portable searchlights and various IR marking devices.

# PHOENIX TRANSMITTER

The Phoenix is the first pocket-sized user-programmable infrared (IR) beacon designed for individual combat identification (CID). It is invisible to the naked eye, but has been seen from as far away as 20 miles with night vision systems. Its primary advantage is its instant no-tool field encoding capability, which allows any user to easily enter and change the flashing code. Any metallic object can be used to enter a unique code, thus allowing units to be distinguished from one another.

## 5000 GEN-3 GOGGLES

- Removeable F/1.3 C-mount Objective Lens
- Built-In IR Illuminator & Low Battery Indicators
- Bright Source Protection Circuitry
- Nitrogen Purged Water Resistant Mil-Spec Housing
- Military Head Mount & Soft Case Included

**Hitek International** 484 El Camino Real, Redwood City, CA 94063 www.nightsight.com. Originally a portable closet manufacturer (no kidding) Hitek was one of the first direct importers of Russian NVD's.

They actually chartered their own planes, bought avgas on, uh, the "gray" market in Moscow and shipped back cargo planes chocked full of Russian scopes.

They now offer almost entirely American scopes at good prices.

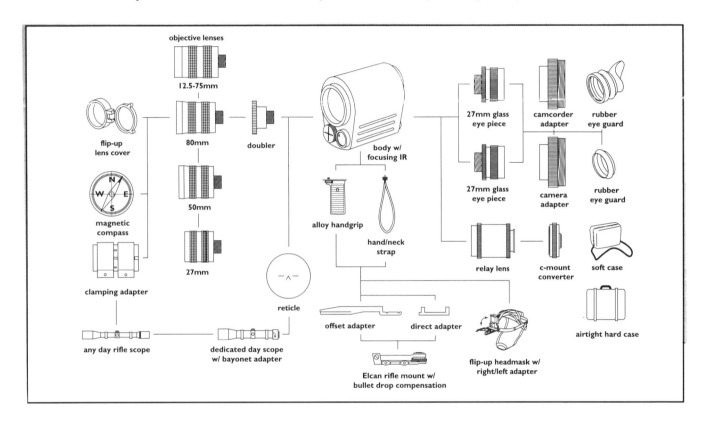

**ITI** POB 381 Westfield, MA 01086. Want to see under a closed door? Thru a wall (well, with a tiny 3mm hole)? Check into the insides of a car door or other closed area?

Very nice fiber optic/lens electronic hybrids that let the common man be a superman. $1,000-$4,000+, resold by many dealers at twice the original price.

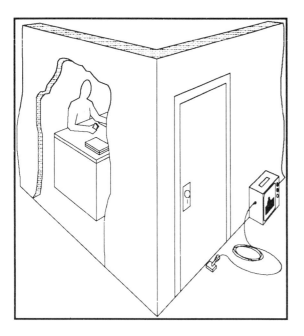

## Model 135301                    Under Door Remote Viewing Kit

**ITI lets you look into a room without opening the door!** Working with a 1/4" under door space, this kit is perfect for monitoring activity in a remote location. Designed with a 15° offset angle, viewing is from the floor up, maximizing the amount of observable area. This kit features a dedicated "C" mount for video camera attachment. Attachable viewing eyepiece included for visual observation.

As with other ITI instruments, the 135301 kit is designed to provide **maximum resolution**, as is required for covert surveillance.

### Specifications
**Under Door RVI**

| | | **Kit includes:** |
|---|---|---|
| Probe Diameter | 5mm (.196") | 1- Under Door RVI |
| Working Length | 3" | 1-Visual Eyepiece Adapter |
| Line of Sight | Offset 15° | 1-Protective carrying case |
| Field of View | 55° | |

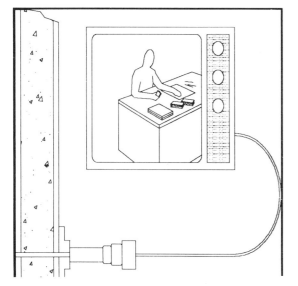

## Model 135460                    Micro Thru-Wall RVI Kit

**Full sight through a 2 1/2mm hole** is possible with our Micro Thru-Wall RVI Kit. Merging maximum resolution, portability, quick setup and low cost makes ITI's Micro Thru-Wall RVI the ultimate in covert surveillance. **Remove yourself completely from your target's line of sight!** The kit features a dedicated "C" mount for video camera attachment, and an attachable viewing eyepiece for visual observation.

The miniature probe allows surveillance into an adjacent room while its offset view permits greater coverage. Detachable wall mount included for supporting of Micro Thru-Wall RVI & video camera.

**Deutsche Optik** POB 7518, San Diego, CA 92167 www.deutscheoptik.com. DO publishes a very slick Sharper Image-like catalog four times a year with everything one could desire in the way of spotting scopes, telescopes, and the like.

Some very nice binoculars in all shapes and sizes from waterproof marine to mini-camoflauge models. Top quality name brands plus the very latest in optical offerings (new coatings, camera-to-spotting scope adapters) make this a serious source for the surveillance minded.

Protection of ... rated Optolyth ... binoculars "excellent" ... ornithological applications.

## ◀ TBG/TBS 80 Fluorite Models

A relatively recent development in high-end optical circles has been the development of crystallized CaF2 (fluorite) lenses. Fluorite is a crystal: it is grown rather than made (like ordinary glass) and its slow growing characteristics and touchy nature make for an expensive and laborious process. However, fluorite is capable of providing extraordinary detail and virtually perfect color resolution in very low light or at high magnification. Put another way, a pure white egret will appear pure white even in dawn or dusk conditions or when seen through a 70x eyepiece. No other combination of glass or coatings can provide such color fidelity and resolution.

We are proud to offer the two finest fluorite spotting scopes on the market today. The Optolyth TBG 80 GA/HD (straight eyepiece mount) and the TBS 80 GA/HD (45 degree eyepiece mount) are rubber armored, weatherproof, nitrogen filled, and built with the finest materials and workmanship that Optolyth has to offer. They are consistently rated as being among the world's finest spotting scopes, and their exceptional clarity and complete lack of color bias is simply unmatched. Fully padded case also included. Not cheap, but worth every penny.

**Vogel-Swarovski Optik** S. Hollow Estate, RR #2, Box 2542 Hallstead, PA 18822. Based in Austria VSO manufactures some of the world's best binoculars, spotting scopes, weapon scopes and now some night vision equipment.

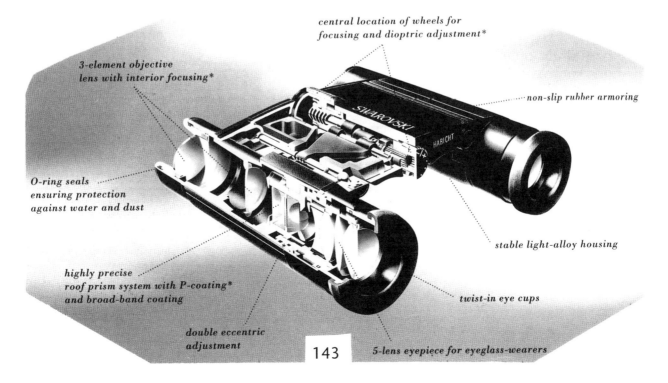

*central location of wheels for focusing and dioptric adjustment\**

*3-element objective lens with interior focusing\**

*non-slip rubber armoring*

*O-ring seals ensuring protection against water and dust*

*stable light-alloy housing*

*highly precise roof prism system with P-coating\* and broad-band coating*

*twist-in eye cups*

*double eccentric adjustment*

*5-lens eyepiece for eyeglass-wearers*

143

**Ashbury International Group, Inc.,** POB 885, Sterling, VA 20167. American distributors of Leica range finding binocular that will locate, distance and record (using built-in GPS) targets, uh, rather sites of interest, up to 4 Km distant.

Great for navigation, pipeline planing, tactical law enforcement, golf, hunting tank or machine gun spotting, and other hobbies.

## Multi-Purpose Binocular Laser Rangefinder

Leica, the worlds leader in precision optical instruments is proud to introduce to the GIS community VECTOR, the worlds only design-built, fully integrated Class I eyesafe binocular laser rangefinder with a precision on-board digital magnetic compass, inclinometer and RS-232 data interface. The VECTOR is a true "intelligent observation system", providing today's GIS professional with a rugged, advanced technology binocular that fully supports GIS data collection missions requiring observation, distance and angle measurement, orientation and positioning. The VECTOR provides GIS data collectors with unfailing high quality performance in the field, even under adverse environmental conditions. Most GIS disciplines share a common requirement for a state-of-the-art, high quality electro-optic data collection device, that will stand up to the rigors of demanding field data collection assignments. The Leica VECTOR is that GIS field data collection device...and more!

**Trans Western Sales**
25422 Trabuco Road, Suite 105, Lake Forest, CA 92630. Manufacturers Reps for Tasco Sport Optics one of the oldest and best OEM rifle and spotting scope, sunglasses and binocular providers in the US, TASCO constantly offers innovations such as multi coated (up to 14 times) lenses for optimum viewing in any conditions.

Trans W. also sells some early generation night scopes. Prices are about as good as they are going to get on these popular products.

568BCR

178RB

565RB

**Stillwater Trading Company** 11969 Livona Lane, Redding, CA 96003 www.stillwtr.com. Makes a marvelous device known as the LE-Adapter. Said MD will connect virtually any camcorder on the market to telescopes, monoculars, binoculars, spotting scopes or night vision equipment.

$130 turns your camcorder into a super surveillance recorder.

The Patented *LE-Adapter* can increase the magnification of your Camcorder 100x or more—day or night—with no loss in your video image clarity.

**Optical Electronics Inc.**, POB 11140 Tucson, AZ 85734. OEM of video still image printers and a rather unique self contained video enhancement unit that can improve the quality of live or recorded images.

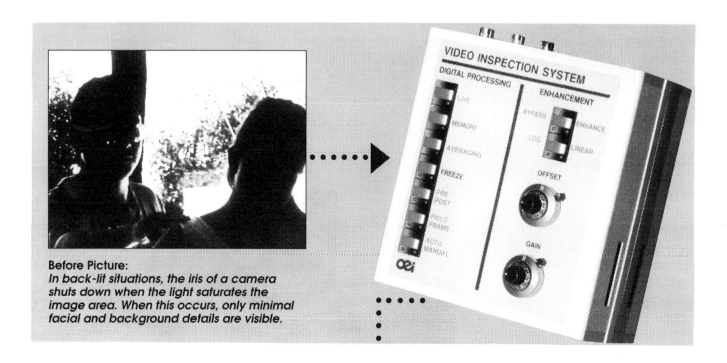

**Before Picture:**
*In back-lit situations, the iris of a camera shuts down when the light saturates the image area. When this occurs, only minimal facial and background details are visible.*

**Maxa Beam** (Peak Beam Systems) 523 Bill Williams Ave., Williams, AZ 86046. Ever had the urge to shine a bright flashlight into the neighbor's window when they're blasting rap music at 2 am?

What if the neighbors live 1 1/2 miles away?

No problem.

Maxa Beam is the world's most powerful handheld searchlight, blasting out 6 million candlepower it claims a *3+ mile* range under perfect conditions and is a solid source at 1 1/2 miles.

This is the same unit you can see on those irritating helicopters that major city police departments fly over your house to make certain you don't sleep at night.

# Maxa Beam Packages

**MBPKG-B**

**Basic Maxa Beam Package** includes:

(1) MBS-410 Maxa Beam Searchlight
(1) MBP-1207 NiCad Rechargeable Battery Module
(1) MBA-6005 Battery Carry Strap
(1) MBP-3100 NiCad Drop-in Trickle Charger

**MBPKG-D**

**Search Systems** POB 80307 Bakersfield, CA 93380. Video cameras mounted on a variety of probes for a variety of purposes including searching for disaster victims to searching for enemies. Most models include audio and either visible or IR lighting.

Professional, expensive systems.

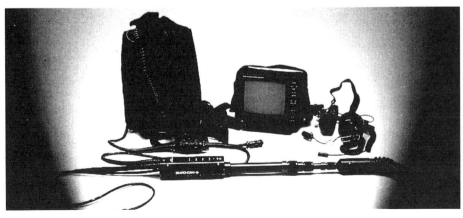

146

**Streamlight** 1030 West Germantown Pike, Norristown, NJ 19403. Some of the best portable lights made – I use a Streamlight. Super bright, rechargeable, adjustable width beam, hit-'em-on-the head construction.

## SCORPION®

* *You could put the 4.9" Scorpion away for 10 years, switch it on and get up to 6,500 candlepower for one full hour. The secret's in the two 3V lithium batteries and Xenon bulb, together in the lightest (4.4oz.), brightest personal light ever built. Ideal as a serious backup or emergency light. Machined aluminum case has rubber armored sleeve, O-ring sealing for moisture resistance, unbreakable Lexan® lens and adjustable spot-to-flood focus.*

**Felix Security Devices** POB 446 Oregon City, OR 97045. Felix is one of the best known suppliers of complete law enforcement surveillance vans. They also offer a high powered IR strobe and now carry some Russian NVD's.

Your flashlight or tactical light is a lot more useful if its beam is flawlessly smooth, and free of dark spots, rings, and other irregularities. This is not something you will find in a typical commercial or consumer flashlight, even in the highest price models of the best known manufacturers. It requires the use of a special reflector surface and precision focusing of the lamp, something best done at the factory and permanently fixed in place. This is what is done with SURE-FIRE lamp/reflector assemblies, and why SURE-FIRE flashlights and tactical lights produce such superb beams.

It is also important to have the right beam spread for the job at hand: narrow for reaching out long distances, medium for general use, and wide for close up work. Unfortunately, you cannot achieve this with a "focusable" flashlight, as all you are really doing is adjusting the flashlight to be out of focus, where it produces an exceptionally poor quality beam complete with irregularities, dark spots, and rings. The solution is to design the reflector for the tightest beam spread needed, and then broaden the beam with a holographic diffusing lens or "BeamShaper", when a broader beam is required for close up work. This is what is done with SURE-FIRE flashlights and tactical lights.

BeamShaper push-fits over bezel.

**Surefire, Laser Products**, Fountain Valley, CA 92708. Probably the most complete line of heavy duty law enforcement type flashlights. Many models feature switchable heads for different applications. Some rechargeable, some lithium powered.

Also IR sources, flashlight pouches and weapon mounted lights. A good catalog, choices for just about every lighting situation.

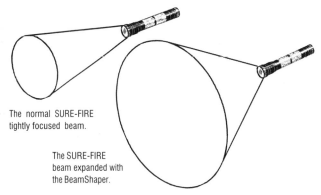

The normal SURE-FIRE tightly focused beam.

The SURE-FIRE beam expanded with the BeamShaper.

**Delta Light** POB 202223, Minneapolis, MN 55420. Delta specializes in the use of LED's to replace normal incandescent lighting systems. They offer direct light bulb screw-in replacement units, and strip illuminators in a number of configurations. The LED light is "pure white" and several times more efficient that any other type of lighting.

Products are great for outdoor, non-mains systems such as camping, perimeter illumination, etc. They also offer LED strips in infrared rather than white light which are ideal for invisible area coverage. My favorite products are the replacement flashlight bulbs in either pure white or IR.

**DL2 & DL2A:** An LED flashlight replacement bulb made in America lasting virtually a lifetime! Replaces a standard PR-2 bulb. Constructed with LED technology - no fragile filament to wear out or break. Uses only the power of standard flashlight bulbs - runs continuously for weeks on one set of batteries! With fewer batteries to throw away, these units pay for themselves in batteries saved. Available in **red, yellow, blue, green, white or infrared light** (prefocused beam) - lights up an area with a 6 foot radius without sacrificing night vision. Fits most 2 cell (AA, C or D) flashlights (80%), while using only 45 mA at 3VDC.
*Order* #DL2 (4% Beam Spread)......................................................................$9.95
*Order* #DL2A (15° Beam Spread – red or amber color only) .........................$4.95

## *OWL EYE* TVC-3000

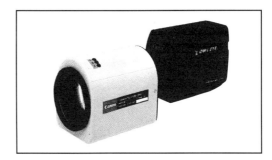

**Wood Surveillance** 400 Buckner Dr., Battle Creek, MI 49015. WS sells the Owl Eye series of enhanced CCD camera lenses as well as a fairly unique video motion detection/recording system. Owl Eye low light amplifiers work in near total darkness (.0009 Lux) when attached to a 1/2" CCD camera.

| Conventional CCD Camera | OWL-EYE |
|---|---|

**Special Features of the TVC-3000:**
- 1/2 inch format with Bayonet Lens Mount
- 3 CCD Image sensor
- Ultra High- Resolution and Brilliant Color Reproduction
- Freeze Frame
- Manual , Remote, or Automatic Operation

# WEAPONS
## And Personal Protection

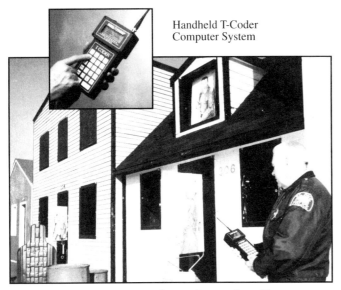

Handheld T-Coder
Computer System

1800 Combat Target System in a combat village

**Duelatron** 4524 Highway 61, St. Paul, MN 55110. Targets that inflate, deflate, run, pivot and more things than I do on Sundays.

All by wireless remote control.

**Laser Devices, Inc.**, 2 Harris Court A4, Monterey, CA 93940 www.tmx.com/alaserdevices. Switchable laser (IR or red) and tactical white light for hittin' da bad guys in any situation from bright sunlight to complete darkness.

ULS-2001 (Combo I)
w/TLS-8R TACTICAL LIGHT

**Lasermax** 3495 Winton Pl., Bldg. B, Rochester NY 14623 www.Lasermax-inc.com. Fits *inside* your gun, weighs 1/4 ounce, never needs re-calibration. Great idea, well thought out and well made.

# PAGER PAL® U.S. PATENT #5570827

## The Ultimate Concealment Systems

*$49.95*

A deep concealment holster, designed for cross draw, the Pager Pal enables the user to carry a concealed handgun anytime pants or shorts are worn. The contoured, fine leather paddle design of the Pager Pal gives great comfort, complete concealability as well as fast access. Your real pager can be substituted for the dummy pager that comes with the Pager Pal. Pager Pals are designed to fit more than fifty handgun sizes. They come in small & large sizes, left & right-hand shooter, and tan or black leather.

**Pager Pal Concealment Systems** 200 W. Pleasantview, Hurst, TX 76054. A variety of concealed holsters, most of which have a phony (well, I suppose one could substitute a real one, just be careful what you answer) pager on the outside of one's pants whereupon gun be on inside.

**Thunderware, Inc.**, POB 2460 Satellite Beach, FL 32937. "invisible" holsters that put your gun where nobody but the brave will look.

Besides you can pick up chicks in singles bars...

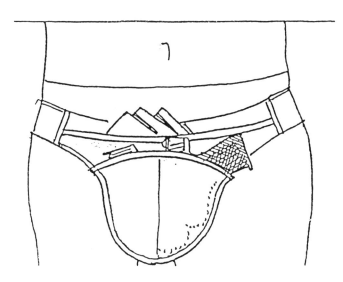

## THE BEST JUST GOT BETTER!
Thunderwear introduces the
### COMBO!

We took the basic Thunderwear holster and made it ambidextrous, providing single or <u>double</u> weapon carry and gave it a full credential pocket for your shield and identification. It can also be used as a hideout for a wireless transmitter.

**Michaels of Oregon** 1710 Red Soils Ct., Oregon City, OR 97045. Both leather and nylon holsters, slings, ammo pouches a very hard to find belly belt holsters.

**Sang Min International Co., Ltd.**, 366 Cheng Ung Rd., Feng Yuan Taichung Hsien, Taiwan, ROC. Shock rods, hand stunners, alarms as well as a couple of vests and shields.

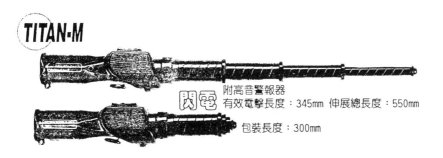

閃電 附高音警報器
有效電擊長度：345mm 伸展總長度：550mm

包裝長度：300mm

手電筒照明

噴催淚辣椒精

**Coronado Leather** 120 "C" Ave., Coronado, CA 92118. Very fashionable purses, shoulder bags, fanny packs and back packs that really do pack.

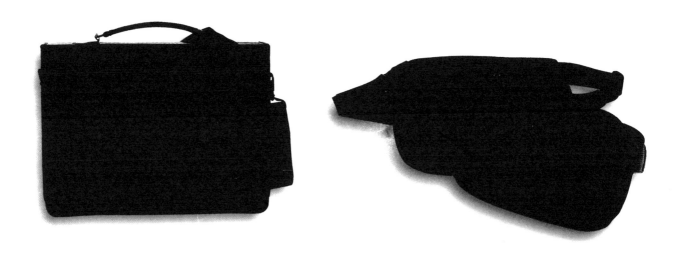

**Gemtech** POB 3538 Boise, ID 83703 www.gem-tech.com. Silencers, surpressed pistols/rifles, and my personal favorite (I had one) the LDE-9 Pengun.

Again only for those with the proper credentials.

**Sound Technology** POB 391 Pelham, AL 35124. Silencers, sniper rifles, training courses and neat stuff.

**Firequest International** POB 315 El Dorado, AR 71731 www.firequest.com. Boy, I could spend all my allowance with these guys. The most fun you can have with your clothes on and not expect to have dinner courtesy of the nice folks at ATF office.

Armor piercing bullets, 12 gauge tear gas shells, bird bombs (a bird bomb, designed for agricultural use only) is basically a M-80 loaded into a 12 gauge shotgun shell.

After traveling for several hundred feet the bomb explodes. Also shotgun a shell that puts out a 250 foot "wall of flame" (who could not have fun with that?). Flechette shells (mean) shells with chain link, shells designed to penetrate car engines thusly rendering said vehicle inoperable, pepper spray in a 12 gauge shell – why spray when you can blast him with elan?

Almost automatic rifle converters (legal ones), 12 gauge pistols for shooting all your new toys, some books and something even I have no idea what the hell one does with – "The Hooker. One shot and you're hooked. This 12 gauge shell is loaded with one large lead ball, a little wire and a hook! If nothing else the hooker is a unique of power and sting"

Okay...

Most things sold to anybody (well, of course not us idiots who live in the People's Republic of California), but there are ways around that.

My wife waited until I went to sleep and immediately hid this catalog somewhere.

I'll find it.

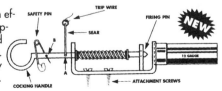

# Individual Assault Kit

**Tactical & Survival Specialties** 1832 S. Main, Harrisonburg, VA 22801. An individual assault kit that would allow one, as best I can tell, to climb a building, protect one's hearing, watch someone welding, hide a pistol, use your flashlight in one of several modes, signal your backup, wedge a door open, beat the shit out of whomever is behind the door with your baton and then restrain him/her/it.

## QUADRANGLE BUCKSHOT
## P/N 4400

QBTM - 8 Quadrangle Buckshot is a substitute for 00 buckshot and intended for applications where 00 is not *effective* or has limited effectiveness. It replaces the .32 caliber lead balls that are 00 buckshot with hardened steel pie-shaped wedges call **Quadrangle Pellets**. These pellets have 6 pointed corners, 7 sharp edges and 5 surfaces each. The geometry of the pellets and the hardness of the metal used makes the QB pellets very effective in penetrating a target. Where a lead 00 pellet must use a significant amount of its energy to break through sheet metal, a QB pellet pierces or slices through the sheet metal like a punch press. This property allows the QB to be used against targets that would defeat ordinary buckshot. It is very effective against automobiles as it will cut right through a windshield without grazing. It can pierce a door and the window glass with sufficient energy to pierce 1/2 inch plywood.

The sharp edges of the QB allows it to cut through the fibers of a Level IIA Kevlar Soft Body Armor Vest. This allows it to be used for close quarter battle against individuals that may be wearing protective armor. It has no effect against Level III armor utilizing ceramic or metal trauma plates. The California Department of Justice tested the QB-8 buckshot against a Level IIA vest that was placed over a block of ballistic gelatin. Seven of eight pellets penetrated the vest completely and penetrated 4 inches into the ballistic gelatin. When fired into bare ballistic gelatin, the pellets gave 10.5 inches of penetration.

**MK Ballistic Systems** 2707 Santa Ana Valley Road, Hollister, CA 95023 www.pnet.net/mk/. 12 gauge based less-than-lethal munitions, door breaching rounds, flash-bangs and some other unique projectiles.

**Arizona Response Systems** 5501 North 7th Ave., Suite 1005, Phoenix, AZ 85013. Glock customizing, special products (holsters, items of interest) and my favorite –

An all-natural Ghillie suit that should hide and protect your fragile little body in almost any situation, unless, of course you find yourself running down Telegraph Avenue in Berkeley, California yelling, "death to the pigs".

In which case you might wish to consider the following product line.

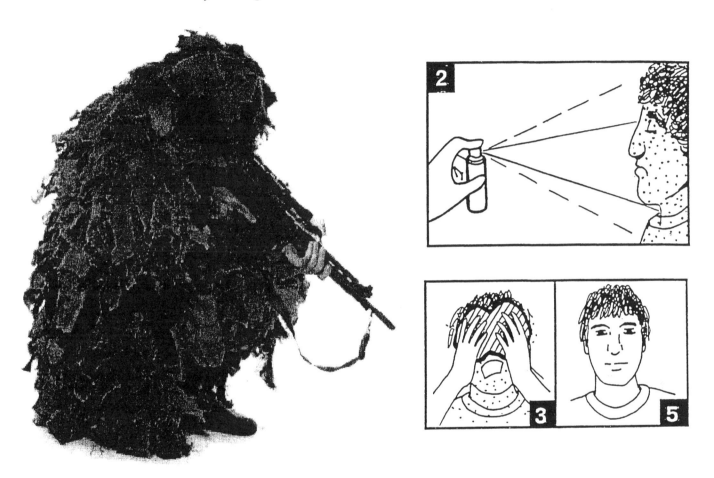

**Aplec Team Incorporated** 201 Rickenbacker, Circle, Livermore, CA 94550. Manufacturers a rather unique line of bio shields, Band-Aids, if you will, counter soldiers in the war between those who use such irritating sprays as OC, CS, CN and Pepper spray.

To make a long story short if one has reason to expect to come into contact with one of these delightful products, either because some evil minded SOB has made it his personal responsibility to cause you massive pain and discomfort, you happen to be in the wrong place at the wrong time, or some other dumb SOB picks your canister and has the Chutzpah to use against you.

At any rate this stuff will reverse the effects in short order. Ideal gift for your College aged son.

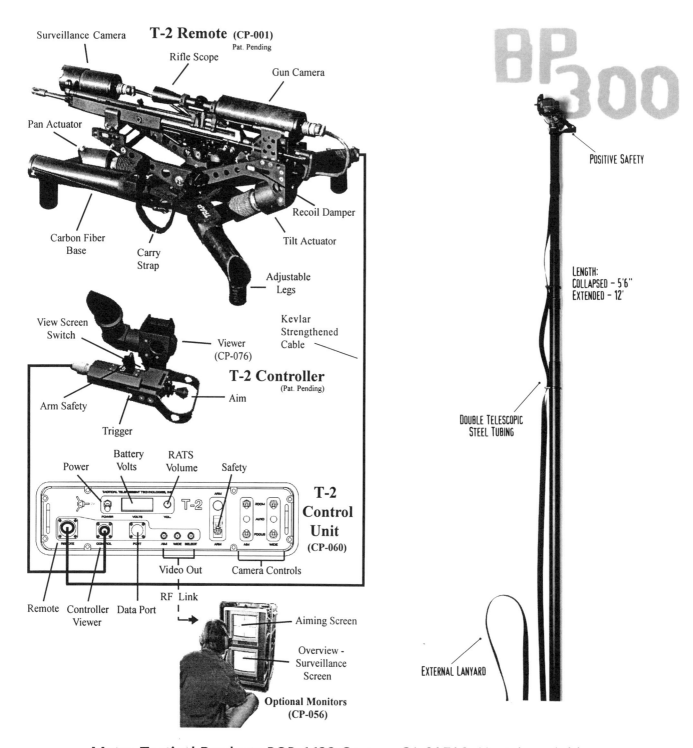

**T-2 Remote** (CP-001)
Pat. Pending

- Surveillance Camera
- Rifle Scope
- Gun Camera
- Pan Actuator
- Carbon Fiber Base
- Carry Strap
- Recoil Damper
- Tilt Actuator
- Adjustable Legs
- Kevlar Strengthened Cable

- View Screen Switch
- Viewer (CP-076)
- Arm Safety
- Aim
- Trigger

**T-2 Controller**
(Pat. Pending)

- Power
- Battery Volts
- RATS Volume
- Safety

**T-2 Control Unit** (CP-060)

- Remote
- Controller Viewer
- Data Port
- RF Link
- Video Out
- Camera Controls
- Aiming Screen
- Overview - Surveillance Screen

**Optional Monitors** (CP-056)

**BP 300**

- POSITIVE SAFETY
- LENGTH: COLLAPSED – 5'6" EXTENDED – 12'
- DOUBLE TELESCOPIC STEEL TUBING
- EXTERNAL LANYARD

**Metro Tactical Products** POB 6633 Corona, CA 91718. Upstairs neighbors playing that stereo *really, really* loud? Never answer the phone when you complain.? Maybe they are hornet's nest of terrorists from some nefarious desert country? Why risk a direct confrontation? As Shakespeare said, "cry havoc and unleash the dogs of war".

Or I say, shove the big stick directly upward and set off the damn grenade...

**Tactical Telepresent Technologies, Inc.,** POB 70812 Point Richmond, CA 94807. Just the thing for those troubling times when you really want to shoot someone with a 50 caliber cartridge but just aren't in the mood for direct confrontation.

Reach out and touch someone by remote control...          156

**Phoenix Systems Inc.,** POB 3339, Evergreen, CO 80437. All those little things you meant to pick up at the supermarket but slipped your mind; pepper gas, locksmithing tools, hidden holsters, saps, batons, flechette filled shotgun rounds, inexpensive Ghillie suits, razor wire and lettuce safes.

No, it's not a safe for lettuce, see, it's safe that *looks like* lettuce.

Artic Camo

Desert Camo

Woodland Camo

**STEALTH GOLF BALLS-** Yes, we now have camo golf balls available in your favorite patterns, Artic Camo, Desert Camo and Woodland Camo. These **three packs** of top quality golf balls make an excellent gift. Order your favorite pattern or an assortment that includes one of each pattern. Don't play golf without them. Great for "improving" your "lie" without being noticed or fudging every chance you get!

**HELLSTORM 2000 The New Generation of "Hellfire"! Completely BATF approved.** Reach near full automatic rates of fire by simply attaching the HELLSTORM to

your trigger guard; installs in minutes. When the unit is installed behind your trigger, it is adjusted to create a "static" condition. This condition is offset when you pull the trigger and countered by your gun's bolt action. You actually "feel" the trigger move against your finger at the same rate your gun would fire if it were converted to full automatic. Comes with complete mounting instructions and official letter of legality. The basic model fits most weapons, including AR15/M16, Mini 14 & 30, and AK's. If you have a SKS, TEC9 or Ruger 10/22, order the specific model indicated below.

**Streicher's** 10911 West Hiway 55, Minneapolis, MN 554411. A law enforcement oriented supplier, of clothing, bullet resistant vests, holsters, flashlights, pepper spray and ammo.

## 10x25 COMPACT BINOCULARS

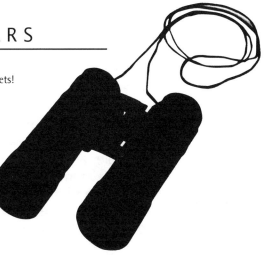

Designed for your tactical applications. Small enough to fit into your BDU pockets!

10 power x 25mm lens. Includes case and neck cord. Camouflage or black.

#BUSH-132516    *Black*    $39.95
#BUSH-132517    *Camouflage*    $39.95

**SEA Technology, Inc.** POB 31151, Albuquerque, NM, 87190-1151.
SEA Laser Dissuader which looks and feels like an ordinary police flashlight, impairs the subject's eyesight temporarily with its glaring beam of high-intensity red light. When the Dissuader is trained on the suspect's face, he or she *cannot* see in the direction of the beam and must look away, close their eyes, or cover them with their hands, giving officers a chance to move in.

The Laser Dissuader's beam is non-harmful to officers and produces the visually disarming glare from as far away as 500 yards at night. The device's beam can be tightly focused to a few inches in diameter for maximum effect or spread to several feet in diameter to illuminate an individual or group.

Because the Laser Dissuader looks like an ordinary flashlight, most suspects initially will not perceive the device as threatening. The Dissuader's non-threatening appearance minimizes the risk of prematurely escalating the confrontation and increases the subject's level of surprise and confusion when they are hit with the beam.

The Laser Dissuader operates in two modes. The continuous mode provides a steady glare, which can give officers time to neutralize an armed or unarmed person. The flicker mode provides a strobe light effect that can cause disorientation and confusion or highlight a target for other officers.

**Life Finder, Inc.** 2007 Bob Wallace Ave. Huntsville, AL 35805-4724 . Somewhere out there, there's a hidden person. His exact position is unknown and he is motivated by only one thought... to elude you and your team. In the past, the only way to find him was by reconnaissance with your team. Many times, because of your environment, your operations were unsuccessful, or worse, resulted in casualties due to unexpected aggression.

In all armed actions there are risks. The **LIFE FINDER LF-3 TM** Thermal Detector Device can help your forces maintain the upper hand in forested regions, through smoke, and in fact any condition in which you need to deploy personnel.

Due to developments over the last twenty years, this technology has been reduced to a hand held device that is simple to use, extremely rugged, reliable, and operates in the most punishing conditions. **LIFE FINDER LF-3 TM** is an extremely accurate and sophisticated piece of equipment. It detects even the slightest changes in thermal signatures. By using this small hand-held device in a sweeping motion, the **LF-3TM** has detected humans at ranges of over 1,000 meters in open areas and through 100 meters of dense forest, day or night. What odes this mean to you? You can detect your opponent or lost person's position and take necessary action. The **LIFE FINDER LF-3 TM** also has a motion mode. With the audio output, you can now do unmanned surveillance.

**Armacel Armor Corp.**, 2255 Pleasant Valley Rd., Camarillo, CA 93012. Vests constructed with Armacel – a non-woven composite which is molded (with resin) much like fiberglass. Used on the Space Shuttle and the Blackhawk helicopter, Armacel is claimed to offer unparalleled protection and comfort.

Drop-in trauma plates are not required as the vest is molded and fused for integral trauma/cardiac protection.

*Sikorsky UH-60A Black Hawk*

*NASA-Boeing Space Station Freedom*

# ARMACEL PROTECTION
## A TWENTY-FIRST CENTURY SOLUTION FOR LAW ENFORCEMENT OFFICERS, GOVERNMENT AGENTS, AND MILITARY PERSONNEL

Armacel vests are designed to defend the upper body's vital organs against ballistic penetration from all angles. In addition, the armor material is resistant to attack by sharp edged instruments, as well as jagged fragments from explosions. It has been certified as meeting National Institute of Justice Standard 0101.03 by the National Law Enforcement and Corrections Technology Center. Armacel armor can also be designed in order to protect against a wide variety of threat levels, up to and including armor piercing ammunition.

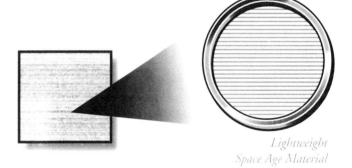

*Lightweight Space Age Material*

**First Choice Armor & Equipment** 45 Emerson Ave., Brockton, MA 02301 www.firstchoicearmor.com. One of the first manufacturers to use a brand new, lightweight fabric which can be rolled into a ball and will withstand over 900 inch LBS from an ice pick.

I've seen it tested and it will. Not necessarily bullet proof at this stage, more anti-knife, but may be available as both by the time you read this.

**National Body Armor** 3809 Plaza Dr., Suites 107-226, Oceanside, CA 92056. OEM of high security body armor for law enforcement and the military, NBA has branched out into the civilian market with vests that don't look like vests.

Designed for TV reporters, photographers, CEO's, doctors and others that may find themsevles peering down the open end of a firearm. Using two different materials vests can be ordered in several different threat levels.

### Shamus Vest

Sam Spade never had it so good! National Body Armor's Shamus Vest is the original Trench Coat converted into solid ballistic protection. Half or full coverage. It's your choice. Available for most garments. Call for details.

### Covert Vest

The perfect vest for concealing ballistic protection while "blending-in" in almost any street situation. Made of strong denim materials, you may supply the jacket or purchase one ready made. Available in Blue or Black, with or without sleeves.

**21st Century Hard Armor** 16710 Hedgecroft, Suite 106, Houston, TX 77060 www.21stcenturyhardaror.com. Kevlar vests in all threat levels plus hard inserts and shields which will stop anything up to an RPG.

**Level IV inserts are designed to protect from 30-06 armor piercing rounds and all lesser threats.**

**They are made of ceramic with a KEVLAR® spall backing.**

**Size: 10" x 12"**

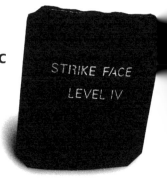

STRIKE FACE LEVEL IV

**Armor Holdings Inc.**, 13386 International Parkway, Jacksonville, FL 32218 www.armorholdings.com. Combining several different fabrics into a composite that claims to be "unquestionably the lightest, most comfortable and wearable vest ever".

**LEADING COMPETITOR'S VEST**

**XTREME ARMOR**™

**PERFORMAX**™

The development of Xtreme Armor™ has also produced a line of performance models. The Xtreme II & IIIA Performax™ features the same unique fusion of materials with additional protection and ballistic performance. Designed to defeat special threats including such foreign rounds as the 7.62 x 25mm Tokarev 86 gr. FMC and the Geco 9mm 124 gr. FMC, the Xtreme Performax™ offers maximum ballistic protection in lightweight, ultra-thin packages. The Xtreme Performax™ packages have already been submitted for international certifications throughout the world.

**Silent Partner Body Armor, Inc.**, 612 Third St., Gretna, LA 70053. One of the best selling law enforcement vest makers around. All SP vests are woven from Kevlar 129, the latest in Mr. DuPont's Kevlar lineup.

**Effective, Easy to Wear, Economical**

## SP "DAYWATCH" ARMOR SERIES

The Silent Partner "Daywatch" Armor Series has been designed to concentrate its ballistic protection over that most critical of areas – the front and back torso "center mass".

The ballistic inserts are constructed of 100% Dupont Kevlar® 129 HT and are reinforced with SPBA's, patented Poly Trauma Reduction System (PTRS). All "Daywatch" Armor is permanently encased in waterproof nylon outer covers.

The "Daywatch" model's scalloped neckline insures a comfortable fit whether you are standing or sitting and the wide range of available strap lengths enables each user to get a great fit every time. Of course, SPBA's twelve-point-adjustable straps are fully removable for easy replacement.

And all "Daywatch" Series vests include a 6"x 8" NFCAS sternum plate.

***National Institute of Justice certified —
Levels IIA and II***

**Shanghai Dongwei Body Armor, Ltd.**, 700 Gui-ping Rd., Shanghai 200233. People's Republic of China. Soft body armor used by the Chinese army, police and even the Japanese.

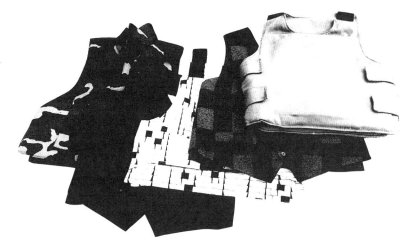

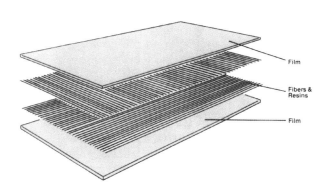

**Shenzhen Mystical Shield Protective Products Co., Inc.,** West 2-F No. 204, Shangbu Industry Area, Zhen Xing Road, Shenzhen, China. God I love these ROC addresses — at any rate this company is a great find. They offer all threat level vests in a couple of the various latest materials.

Dyneema Fiber which resembles Spectra Fiber (Allied Signals) but claims a better protection vs. weight ratio, and Twaron, the hottest new, Kevlar-like fabric around.

Prices are very, very good. Utilized by both the Chinese and German pooleece...

# Dyneema Fiber

In the 1930's, the basic theory of super-strength polyethylene was existed. In 1979 N.V.DSM invented Dyneema fiber and gel spinning technique, which were patented by them. The fiber has models of SK60, SK66, SK75 as well as the newly-developed SK77, strength of which is 10 to 15 times of steel. Spectra fiber, manufactured by Allied Signal in 1985, has the same technical performance as Dyneema but is only equivalent to Dyneema SK66.

采用克维拉或图瓦隆紧密
地编织的防弹材料

**US Armor** 11843 E. Smith Ave., Sante Fe Springs, CA 90670. One of the first vest makers and the first to offer Kevlar protection for less than $200, US is still around and still affordable.

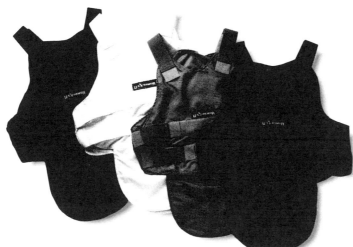

**Colors**: Black, White, Navy Blue, and Tan.

**Other advantages of INTERA Machine Washable Outer Carrier:**

* Doesn't Shrink or Fade
* Odor, Soil, and Mildew Resistant
* Dries almost immediately
* Stronger and longer wearing

**Protech Armored Products, Inc.,** 158 Hubbard Ave., Pittsfield, MA 01201 www.protecharmored.com. Tactical body armor, concealable same, hard inserts, shin guards, briefcases, shields.

**Protective Apparel Corporation Of America** 148 Cedar Place, Norris, TX 37828. Wide line of police and military type vests using Kevlar and Spectra Shield.
**Ballistic Systems Inc.,** 14219 Aston, Houston, TX 77040. Bullet proof glass, security enclosures and a very nice bullet resistant clipboard.

**Safariland** 3120 East Mission Blvd., Ontario, CA 91761 www.safariland.com. Besides a complete line of harnesses and equipment carrying gear they over Kevlar blunt trauma vests as well as being one of the first companies to over vests made from Twaron, the newest, lightweight vest material.

Shock Plates

CoolMax™ T-Shirt

PolyMax Garment

CoolMax™ Garment

Spare Garment

Quilted Garment

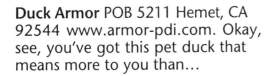
Raid Garment

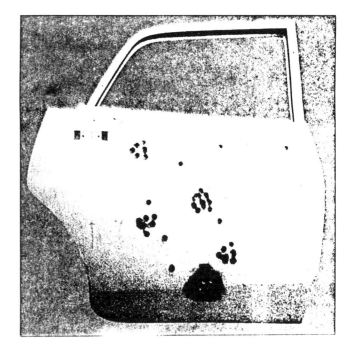
Carry Bag

The Magnum-Lite is Safariland's most affordable ballistic sandwich, offering the ideal balance of price, comfort and protection.

The Magnum-Lite is made exclusively of ultra-soft, lightweight Twaron®2000 Microfilament. Our unique Micro-Lamination process strengthens and reinforces the front panel to spread the energy of an impacting bullet over a wider area. It also helps protect against blunt trauma.

The Magnum-Lite ballistic sandwich is NIJ Certified under the 0101.03 standard for both wet and dry ballistic performance at Levels IIA, II and IIIA.

Please review the Product Matrix (in back) for current threat and style availability.

**Duck Armor** POB 5211 Hemet, CA 92544 www.armor-pdi.com. Okay, see, you've got this pet duck that means more to you than...

Okay, bad joke, on the other hand if you could duck, why would you need armor?

DA will equip you personal vehicle with bullet proof inserts in one or more doors, and if requested replace the glass with transparent ballistic glass/plastic.

# COVERT ENTRY

**MBA** 101 Edgewood Plaza Dr., Nicholasville, KY 40356. Very professional supplier (read locksmiths, law enforcement here) of unique tools for opening everything from car doors to safe deposit boxes.

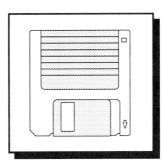

## SAFE OPENING SOFTWARE

MBA is pleased to offer a variety of top notch software aimed at the security industry. These programs are for IBM-PC® or compatible hardware and are very user friendly. The safe software includes:

**SOS (Safe Opening Simulator):** Designed to teach safe identification and trouble shooting for locks that won't open with a combination.

**CAM:** A program designed to teach manipulation with an emphasis on wheel shadowing and memory of wheel placement. Includes a manipulation tutorial with basic combination lock function, lock part I.D., and the theory of manipulation.

## IMPRESSIONING KEYS

These special impressioning keys are designed to open various models of high security "dimple" key locks. The appropriate key is prepped, then inserted into the keyway of the lock. The key is then rocked back and forth "impressioning" style and within minutes the lock opens. No filing or cutting of any kind is required and the keys are re-usable.

#MB13 KABA 8.............$19.50
#MB14 KESO 2000........$19.50

**T- N -T Tools Inc.,** 4691 W. Tufts Ave., Denver, CO 80236. Five tools in one (double your pleasure, double your fun, it's five tools, five tools in one) opening and intervening at houses, auto accidents etc.

The TOOL allows you for "force entry, chop padlocks, free stuck parties and make wellness (sic) calls."

**TRITECH Associates, Inc.,** 2314 Tapestry CT., Toms River, NJ 08755. A couple interesting products including a catch-all kit for picking and impressioning as well as an idea borrowed from the CIA (actually, I believe it was the OSS) that allows one to duplicate a key from just a few moments of possession time.

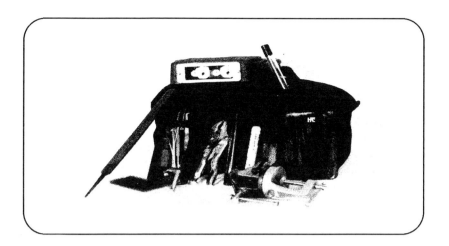

## Tactical Entry Kit
## Model TEK - 2

The Model TEK - 2 kit contains the tools necessary for the entry technician to practice and perform surreptitiously lock entry. The kit contains three different set of tools: 1.) Lock impressioning tool 2.) Lock picking and bypassing tool 3.) Lock servicing and practicing tool (for picking and impressioning practice).

The lock impressioning tool set consists of an impressioning file, a key blank holder and a small flashlight. The file is the most critical component when impressioning a lock. The file included in this kit is specially selected, it gives the best cut and leaves the right finish. This enables the user to "get the marks." With this file, impressioning aids are not needed. The key blank holder grips the key securely so that it will not move during the bump and bind. The flashlight is included for learning how to impression in the dark.

The lock bypass and pick tool set contains picks for general use. This includes pin tumbler, wafer disk and double-sided wafer disk. The bypass tools are for use against warded padlocks. Included also are various sizes of padlock shackle shims.

The lock servicing tools include a lock cylinder plug follower set, lock cylinder/plug shim set and broken key extractors.

The practicing tool set includes a bench top vise and several fixtures and jigs. These allow mounting a lock on a workbench to practice picking or impressioning.

**Steve Arnold's Gunroom** POB 68, Dexter, OR 97431. A good place to buy a variety of lock picks, books about picking locks and books about other topics of interest.

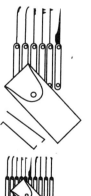

**LOCKAID**
Specifically designed to pick tumbler locks. Designed over thirty years ago to aid law enforcement agencies. Consists of tension wrench, three needles and Lockaid "Gun." Prices include a copy of the book "Lock Picking Simplified."
**$69.95**

**PIX MODEL 13**
This deluxe yet compact kit features 11 of the most commonly used tools. Comes in a slim cowhide leather case for discreet undercover operatives. As a special bonus, a 5 piece set of warded picks is included. A 16 piece set total. Also included, a copy of "Lockpicking Simplified." Receive all this at a low price of:
**$42.95**

**PXP 8**
- Shirt pocket size
- Top grain Cowhide Leather
- Has 8 picks, Tension Wrenchs & Broken Key Extractor
- All Picks with Metal Handles
- Copy of Lockpicking Simplified
**$24.95**

**PXP 10**
- Shirt Pocket Size
- Top Grain Cowhide Leather
- Has 13 Picks, Tension Wrenchs & Broken Key Extractor
- All Picks with Metal Handles
- Copy of Lockpicking Simplified
**$34.95**

**Broco, Inc.,** 8690 Red Oak St. R, Cucamonga, CA 91730. www.brocinc.com. OEM of "burning bars" - basically hollow steel rods into which one forces bottled oxygen and ignites.

That's right; the steel burns, at about 10,000 degrees. This rod will cut through steel doors, railroad rails, spare battle ship parts and us, safes...

When lives are at stake and time is of the essence, gaining entry quickly and effectively is fundamental to achieving your mission and to the protection of your operators. **BROCO's PC/TAC Tactical Cutting Torch** was created to meet the specialized requirements of tactical cutting operations, this ultra-lightweightl system is engineered to provide the greatest cutting capability and reliability in a man-carried torch system. Backpacked in the operational mode, the PC/TAC is fully half the weight of commercial cutting kits, yet it provides the capability of cutting 12 linear feet of 1" thick steel.

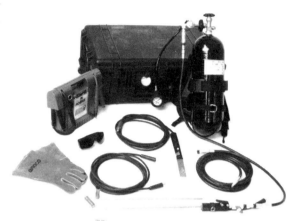

The PC/TAC is not for just rapid entry, but rapid response. Setup is fast and easy. The use of hand-tighten fittings and quick connects means no tools are required for assembly or disassembly.

**Royal Arms** POB 6083 Woodland Hills, CA 91365. One of my favorite methods of "quick" entry is personified by the 12 gauge "breacher" shotgun and frangible entry rounds. The idea here is to blow hinges off doors, knock out locks and kill cross-bolts without killing anyone inside the room (or one's fellow breachers).

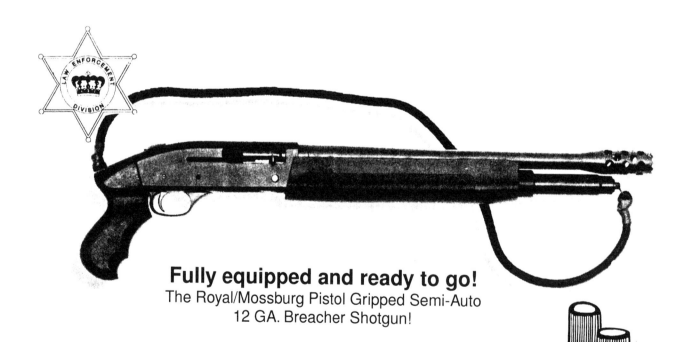

### Fully equipped and ready to go!
The Royal/Mossburg Pistol Gripped Semi-Auto
12 GA. Breacher Shotgun!

# TACTICAL ENTRY AND LESS LETHAL 12 GA. ROUNDS

All frangible and Clayvon rounds are supplied colorcoded for quick identifications.

**B-Safe Industries, Inc.**, POB 153, Scarsdale, NY 10583. Spreaders, pushers, grabbers, peelers, burners, breakers, climbers and hooks for doors, gates, windows, locks etc.

Very interesting catalog.

**1** Place to fit inside door frame, using Third Hand Sling. Instantly adjusts to any size: 26" - 46".

**2** Pump to extend hydraulic piston. Just a few strokes will do!

**3** Open sesame! Remove from door frame.

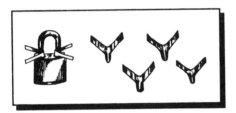

**L451-20 PADLOCK SHIM PICK SET**
20 shims, 5 piece sets, each of four different sizes. Opens most padlocks on the current market. Instructions included.

**E505-18 DUCKBILL BREAKER**
Outstanding tool. Insert duckbill into lock shackle, hit with sledge. Open sesame! Padded handle.

**Security Resources, Inc.**, POB 15532, Pensacola, FL 32514. A locksmith oriented supplier of various tools and one of the most complete selection of "how-to" (pick, impression, open) books around.

**The 1997 FRAMON Depth and Space Manual is now available.** Over 330 pages of information including more than 90 new charts. Spacing block numbers and progressive spacings included.
**FDM-DSM   $65.00**

**FRAMON Impressioning Tool**
Makes impressioning easy! Locks the key blank into place quickly and easily with a simple twist of the wrist. The all metal construction holds the key in a vise-like grip, and there is no wrench to lose. Automatically keeps your hand on the centerline of the lock so you get better marks.

169

**Shomer-Tec** Box 28070, Bellingham, WA 98228 offers a number of lock picking and entry supplies from "common" lockpicks, tubular picks, as well as a couple of "cut away" clear locks that allow the aspiring lockpicker to practice his trade.

Shomer-Tec also offers (law enforcement only) the Electronic Garage Door Opener. Regular garage door openers work one of several basic frequencies. Each individual door is protected by a digital code, allowing thousands of openers to be placed in a housing development with no cross opening problems.

Shomer-Tec's unit works the most popular frequencies and will open many common garage doors and electronic gates.

# ELECTRONIC GARAGE DOOR OPENER

The Electronic Garage Door Opener is a unique electronic tool designed for specialized law enforcement applications. It functions as a "universal" garage door opener, opening nearly all of the two leading brands of remote garage door opening systems in the U.S.—Stanley® and Genie®.* It also opens some of their automatic gate systems. The Garage Door Opener features completely automatic, one-button operation. Designed and manufactured exclusively for law enforcement/governmental usage. Applications include deployment as a law enforcement entry tool for SWAT and dangerous warrant service operations, affording a quieter and safer entry option which increases the element of surprise and consequent increased officer safety, as a non-forcible entry option for firefighters, and as an entry device for authorized federal agency covert operations and SEAL/Special Forces military missions in urban environments. Size: $7^{1}/_{2}$" x $3^{3}/_{4}$" x $1^{1}/_{4}$". Powered by one 9-volt battery (included). NOTE: Restricted sale item —available to governmental agencies and law enforcement <u>only</u>.

**Tung Shih Technology** 7F-10 Ssu Wei Road, Hsinchu, Taiwan. OEM of remote control transmitter duplicators. These amazing devices will duplicate most frequencies and codes in a generic unit provided by the duplicator.

Also known as code grabbers, one simply has to have the unit within range and a new opener will be manufactured on the spot.

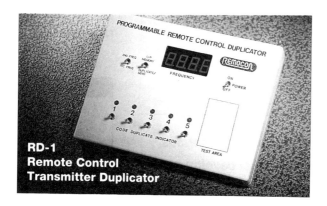

RD-1
Remote Control
Transmitter Duplicator

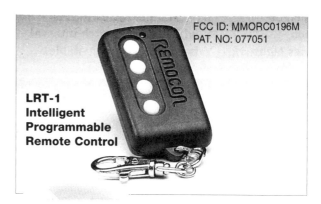

FCC ID: MMORC0196M
PAT. NO: 077051

LRT-1
Intelligent
Programmable
Remote Control

**Intelligence Incorporated** 3555 S. El Camino Real, San Mateo, CA 94403 www.intelligence.to (no "net", no "com"). II carries several unique covert entry products including the Cobra Pro electronic lockpick.

The "electronic" lock pick was invented  20 odd years ago by a locksmith who wanted a simple, in-the-field method to open pin tumbler locks (the most common locks in the world) with no damage and little commotion. He took what was, at the time, one of the most successful quick-pick methods, the Lockaid pick gun and refined the concept.

The pick gun works by inserting a thin needle "pick" into the shear line of a pine tumbler and then suddenly bouncing the top pins away from the bottom pins.

This action frees the tumblers for a split second so the cylinder can be turned with a tension wrench, opening the lock. The pick gun depends on a number of variables being not-so-variable at the correct time including spring tension, position, force and so on.

The locksmith took the same needle pick and coupled it to an electric motor which drives an eccentric cam that bounces and re-bounces the tumblers against each other several times a second, creating a series of opening windows.

Years later II offers the Cobra Pro, machined from aircraft grade aluminum utilizing B and D Quick Charge 18 volt batteries and a high torque German motor.

II offers a couple of good videos designed to teach the art of covert entry, B and E, A to Z II and Superpicking. In the latter both the inventor of the electronic lock pick and the California lock picking champion attack 20 some unmodified, pin tumbler locks including Schlages, Kwicksets, and a variety of other common locks With the Cobra Pro.

The average time to open each lock varies from 3-20 seconds.

Intelligence Incorporated as distributes one of the most amazing entry tools to ever hit the market is the brainchild of another well known locksmith who decided there had to be a way to open most doors *even those protected by super high security Medico type locks* without too much hassle and without destroying the lock.

After several years of experimentation he finalized the design on a device known as the Mule Tool. This system, consists of a number of pieces of rolled steel, bent in particular shapes, some plastic string, a tab or two, a pad of special gripping material and a wedge.

What can the Mule Tool do?

- Open normal key-in-knob cylinder locks as found on most doors, *regardless of the type of lock involved.*
- Open deadbolt locks, again without regard to the creed or color of the lock involved as long as it does not use a key on the inside of the door to open the lock.
- Pop open panic bars from the outside of the door.
- Defeat in-floor door blocking bars in a couple of seconds.
- *Re-lock deadbolts from the inside* after the agent leaves the vicinity.

The Mule Tool system works by sliding underneath any door with a tiny bit of clearance between the door and the ground, reaching up, "grabbing" the knob, or deadbolt latch, from the inside and then turning it to open the door from the inside.

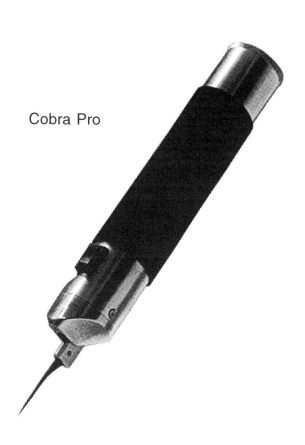

Cobra Pro

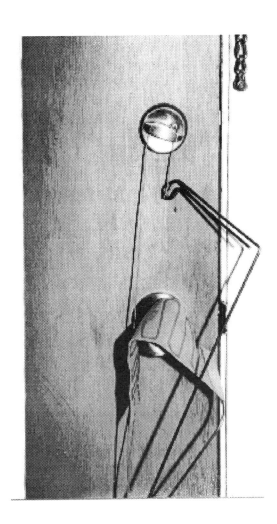

**T.E.E.S.** POB 1345, Southaven, MS 38671. Obviously law enforcement only these nice people (ex SAS) teach explosive handling and explosive entry. Having taken one of these courses (not from his particular school) I can tell you if your chief owes you a favor make him send you through.

What a kick...

**Dakota Alert, Inc.,** POB 130 Elk Point, SD 57025. Wireless driveway alarms and security equipment. Very reasonably priced motion activated alert (500' range), wired metal detectors to let you know anytime a vehicle enters or leaves your place, auto telephone dialers with PIR, smoke, power off alarm capabilities.

# Wireless Motion Drive Alerts

Item #1 . . . 500' Range . . . . . . . . . . . . . $219

Wireless Motion Alerts are very popular units because they are easy to install and will detect both vehicles and people walking. The radio operated drive alert consists of 2 parts - a transmitter and a receiver with 1 whistle. The receiver can be located in your house and plugged into a standard wall outlet. The weatherproof outside transmitter, operated by a 9 volt battery that normally lasts 6 months to 1 year, should be located in the area of your driveway. The transmitter sends out an invisible beam approximately 80 feet. The beam may be pointed in any direction since there is no reflector needed at the end of the beam. If a vehicle or person enters this area, the transmitter, which detects motion, will send a radio signal up to 500' back to the receiver in the house. This sounds a small whistle for approximately 3 seconds to alert you and then shuts off automatically. In the event that you do not want the whistle to sound at any particular time, the receiver is equipped with an on-off switch.

The small transmitter (approximately 5" by 5") can be mounted on a tree, post, building, etc. up to 80 feet back from your driveway. It should be mounted about 3 feet high to allow small animals to walk in the area without being detected. The transmitter will detect large animals such as deer, but is not bothered by the motion of trees and shrubs.

**Slide Lock Tool Company, Inc.,** 1166 Topside Rd., Louisville, TN 37777. A system which utilizes only a few tools (which are bent/manipulated according to the instruction book) in order to open virtually any car on the street.

Also available from a number of dealers.

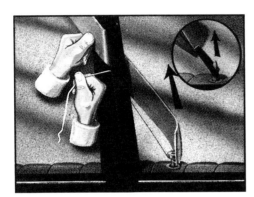

**MERCEDES STRIP:** Superior, high strength .080 inch Lexan®. Banded at one end for high security straight shaft lock buttons, strung the other end with braided pull line for mushroom type lock buttons. Assigned to many more models other than Mercedes.

**SERPENT TOOL:**
**Stainless**
Large and small ends for varied door widths.

**PORSCHE TOOL:**
**Stainless**
Now you can open electric driven lock motors from Germany, including newer BMWs and other manufacturers.

**Spy Headquarters** 125 East Northern Ave., Phoenix, AZ 85020. After the great spy shop busts most closed their doors and wandered off into the sunset, or, in some cases, jail. A few dropped the offensive materials and stayed in business.

Such is SH.

Large catalog of others people's stuff –

Besides the attempt-to-be-legal surveillance devices they have some interesting lock picking and, for that matter, lock them-up stuff.

Worth checking into for general reference, ES and entry.

Dan Gibson mics, pepper spray, extended play recorders, covert video, handcuffs, lockpicks, recording briefcases, Tele-Monitor 2000, batons, a couple of useful counter measures items fake "novelty" bombs and, guess what?

Prices are not too bad! Definitely not the usual 800% "has the word spy in the title" markup.

A special note for lock pick folks – The best lock pick set I have ever used (an opinion shared by every locksmith I've loaned my set to) is called a Falle Pick set.

This unusual set is hand crafted from *stainless steel* and, besides the plentiful pick supply, incorporates the most unusual and useful "circular" tension wrenches.

These adjustable wrenches apply an even pressure to all areas of the lock plug without using pick space.

They really work.

Entire set is packaged in a roll up case.

Bad news is the set is made, one at a time, in England and is not plentiful in the US. More expensive than traditional stamped or spring steel, this set is worth every penny.

Available from MBA.

*Last minute note:* One can now purchase the amazing Falle tension wrenches from MBA without springing for the entire pick set.

**Senstar-Stellar** 1223 Innsbruck Dr., Sunnyvale, CA 94089. Major OEM of unusual intrusion detection and prevention systems. Buried sensor cables, microwave perimeter protection, video motion detection systems, infrared light sources, even a battery operated, portable "radar fence".

# MAGAZINES AND NEWSLETTERS

**A**merican Society for Industrial Security. POB 1409 Alexandria, VA 22313. Great monthly magazine, good books, training and certification for security specialists.

**Association OF Professional Police Investigators (APPI)** 7107 Gettysburg Richmond, TX 77469. The Police Investigator, quarterly magazine. Covers all aspects of criminal investigation, topics include crime scene investigation, evidence collection, and interview techniques.

**Backlisted!411 The official Hackers Magazine** 411 Subscription Dept., POB 2506 Cypress, CA 90630.

**Boardwatch Magazine** 8500 W Bowles Ave. Suite 210 Littleton, CO 80123.

**BRB Publications, Inc.** 4653 Lakeshore Suite 3, Tempe, AZ 85282. Very complete line of books for investigators and information providers. DMV records, courthouse contact information, record providers, much more.

**Competitive Intelligence Review** John Wiley & Sons 605 Third Avenue New York, NY 101058 www.scip.org.

**Company Business** Company Business Inc., 8038 W. Sample Road, Suite 130, Margate, FL 33065. Monthly publication on CIA weapons, training technology, communications, activities and "current situations."

**Council of International Investigators** POB 61 Ambler PA 19002-4921. Annual Summary of Seminars, monthly newsletter.

**Covert Intell Letter** Horizone POB 67 St. Charles, MO 63302. Indicates trends regarding: espionage, terrorism, assassinations, paramilitary operations, raids, and other small-unit military operations. Attempts to provide sources and points of view not ordinarily available.

**CovertAction Quarterly** Covert Action Publications, Inc., 1500 Massachusetts Ave. NW, Rm. 732, Washington, DC 20005. Covers intelligence policies and operations, and U. S, foreign and domestic policy with particular attention to issues of repression in industrialized nations and The Third World.

**CRB Research Books, Inc.** POB 56 Commack, NY 11725-0056. Great "underground" book publisher – mostly radio/scanner oriented.

**The CyberSkeptic's Guide to Internet Research** BiblioData 131 Taylor Street Needham, MA 02194 www.bibliodata.com.

**The Daily Hound** Lynn Peavey Company 14865 W. 105th Street, Kenexa KS 66285-4100. Newsletter on finrgerprints and forensics.

**The Eagle** POB 6303 Corpus Christi TX 78466. Official journal of the International Security and Detective Alliance. The Eagle combines classified ads with product reviews, operational tips and items-of-interest to detectives and security folk.

**Eden Press** POB 8410 Fountain Valley, CA 92728. Best all time identification (ID) book/information source.

**FBI Law Enforcement Bulletin** For the first time in history anyone can subscribe to the FBI's in-house newsletter. Order direct from our old friend the Superintendent of documents, Government Printing Office, Washington, D. C. 2042. Ask for list ID FBIEB.

**The Financial Privacy Report** POB 1277, Burnsville, MN 55337.

**The Florida Private Investigator.** PIAF POB 620712 Orlando, FL 32862-0712. www.pimall.com/piaf/index/html. A very good state journal, worth subscribing even if you aren't in Florida.

**The Freebooter** POB 489, St. Peter Port, Guernsey GY1 6BS, Channel Islands.

**Information Broker** Burwell Enterprises 3724 FM 1960 W Suite 214, Houston, TX 77068. Newsletter for professional information providers. Tips on searching plus the business end of the business.

**Information Security** 106 Access Rd., Norwood, MA 02062 www.infosecuritymag.com. Concerned with computer and net security. Good product reviews.

**Information Solutions** Information Plus (America) Inc., 14 Lafayette Square, Suite 2000 Buffalo, NY 14203-1920. Recent themes have included: Pricing intelligence; sales organization intelligence; new product intelligence.

**Intelligence Incorporated.** 3555 South El Camino Real #309, San Mateo, CA 94403. www.intelligence.to. Books, videos, CD-ROM's (such as this particular publication) as well as others on investigations, surveillance, covert entry, people tracking.

Also what I consider a very nice newsletter.

Of course, I edit it...

**International Footprint Association (IFA)** Brings together, on a social basis, conscientious law enforcement personnel and others interested in improving knowledge of law enforcement problems.

**The Investigator Gazette**, Atlas Information Services Inc., 113 Prince Charles Ct., Collington Harbour, NC 27948. A very well done newsletter for PI's with many people tracking tips, pretext ideas, sources and products.

**IPEC News** 305 Ballards Lane, London, N1P 8NP England. "A service news publication to help police and law enforcement keep up with developments in equipment, vehicles, services and occupational problems on a worldwide basis". A collection of product reviews and paid ads for surveillance and tactical equipment, my gut feeling is you get it free if you write on a letterhead.

**The Journal of Counterterrorism & Security International** Counterterrorism, Inc. POB 10265 Arlington, VA 22210. Quarterly publication – very slick, very well written.

Recent articles have included; Combating Nuclear, Chemical, Biological Materials and Narcotics Smuggling, Executive Protection: Threat Assessment and Shooting with Night Vision.

**Law and Order** 1000 Skokie Blvd., Wilmette, IL 60091. For the rank and file cop/investigator. Good, hands-on material.

**Law Enforcement Technology** 445 Broad Hollow Road, Melville, NY 11747. *Free to qualified professionals.* Other, simpler folk need to cough up $60 per year. Try to be a qualified professional. A good, slick magazine with articles like, " Cutting Cocaine Lines Short", or "Community Policing On Horseback", LETN also carries ads and product reviews for new items of interest to cops and security people.

**Law Enforcement Product News** 100 Garfield St., Denver CO 80206. A large format, glossy magazine/newsletter that runs display ads for products aimed at the security and law enforcement fields.

**LITA Newsletter. Library Systems Newsletter.** American Library Association 434 Downer Aurora, IL. 60506.

**Loompanics Unlimited.** POB 1197 Port Townsend, WA 98368 www.lomponics.com. World's largest underground publisher of books from: Becoming a Successful Mass Murder or Serial Killer – The Complete Handbook, "Ready for that exciting career change you've been dreaming about? Are you lusting for fame, sex, and power? Then this is the book for you", to The Poor Man's Ray Gun.

Catalog $3.00, in itself, very entertaining reading.

**Monitoring Times** published by Bob Grove and the folks at Grove Enterprises, POB 98, Brasstown, NC 28902. MT has come into its own as a useful publication for anyone interested in monitoring the airwaves or communication security.

**Nuts and Volts Magazine** 430 Princeland ct., Corona , CA 91719. N&V started life as a moderate, Computer Shopper/Hemmings type rag with classified ads (and no articles) for the folks who wait anxiously for each issue of Popular

Electronics. In the early days we tried to advertise in them, only to be told, "we do not want to encourage hackers or people involved in surveillance". The ads alone are worth the subscription price.

**Paladin Press.** POB 1307 Boulder, CO 80306. www.paladin-press.com. The best book publisher in the world, bar none.

**Privacy Journal** POB 28577 Providence, RI 02908. Privacy in a Computer Age. Concerned with new technology impact on privacy, individual rights and the confidentiality of data as well as legislation and regulations concerning credit, medical, financial and government records. Also discusses wire taps, polygraphs, electronic surveillance.

**Private Investigators Connection** Thomas Publications, Inc. POB 33244 Austin, TX 78764 Provides information for private investigators.

**The Privacy & Security Review** Thin Man & Associates 4309 Hatch North Las Vegas, NV 89030 Provides information on issues of privacy and security for citizens to use to protect them selves from intrusion and loss from the government , businesses, and criminals. Features include Letters, As We Go To Press, feature Article and Actual Case Histories.

**PI Magazine** 755 Bronx, Toledo, OH, 43609. A relatively new quarterly publication aimed at private investigators and people who like reading about them, PIM touches on surveillance and investigative work as well as providing interviews with notables in this field, reviewing books and some actual entertainment.

**The Police Chief** 515 N. Washington St., Ste. 400, Alexandria, VA 22314-6767.

**Police Magazine** 6300 Yarrow Dr., Carlsbad, CA 92009.

**Police and Security Bulletin** Lomond Publications, Inc., POB 88 Mt. Airy, MD 21771.

**Police and Security News** POB 330 Kulpsville, PA 19443. An *excellent* buy, P&SN is a large format, newsprint monthly with articles and ads of interest to security, law enforcement and surveillance types.

One of the better items in this book.

**The Professional Investigator Newsletter** 2836 Stafford Place Salt Lake City, UT 84119.

**Security** 44 Cook St., Denver, CO 80206. Alarm dealer oriented, carries some products and press of interest.

**Security Directors Digest** Washington Crime News Services 2918 Prosperity Ave., Suite 318, Fairfax, VA 22031-3334. A weekly report on Corporate, Commercial and Industrial Security. Presents and discusses case histories of computer theft, such as duplication of software, computer robbery of monies and stealing computer time. Reviews laws, litigation, and court decisions.

**Security Management** 1655 N. Fort Myer Dr., Suite 1200, Arlington, VA 22209. A very professional magazine on all aspects of security including surveillance and communications. The official journal of the Association of Industrial Security. Product releases, good articles, occasional book reviews.

**Security Technology News** 1201 Seven Locks Road, Potomac, MD 20854. An 8 pages news letter that deals with breaking stories about Smart Credit cards, new legislation on communication technology, and some new product reviews.

**Security Intelligence Report** Interests, Ltd., 8512 Cedar St. Silver Spring, MD 20910-4322. Individuals in intelligence, law enforcement, security, military, embassy, and other protection services.

**Security Law Newsletter** Crime Control Institute & Crime Control Research Corporation 1063 Thomas Jefferson St. NW Washington DC 20007. Security professionals and corporate security.

**Security Letter** 166 E. 96th St. New York, NY 10128. contains "solution-oriented information on security and protection of assets from loss," particularly for executives concerned about the following: internal checks and controls, personnel practices, management of change, fraud and embezzlement, business crime trends, security, and urban terrorism.

**South Florida Investigators Association Journal** South Florida Investigators Association POB 891 Ft. Lauderdale, FL 33302.

**Thomas Investigative Publications, Inc.** POB 33244 Austin, TX 78764. Ralph Thomas publishes a wide variety of investigator oriented materials.

**THUD** The hacker's underground digest. THUD magazine POB 2521 Cypress, CA 90630.

**Top Secret.** POB 23097 Albuquerque, NM 87192 www.tsc-global.com. Publishers of down and dirty reports, some books and occasionally some equipment (well, they don't actually "publish" the equipment). Hacking, answering machine cracking, computer viruses, ATM machine secrets.

Good stuff.

**Varro Press** POB 8413 Shawnee Mission, KS 66208. Serious book publishers for SWAT cops, bodyguards, security specialists.

**2600** "The Hacker Newsletter" POB 752 Middle Island, NY 11953-0099. Run by those nice folks (and their kids) who brought you TAP in the 60's, this is the real thing – computer, phone, communications hacking. Articles, ads, tips, phone numbers, meetings of similar minds. Subscribe.

# TRAINING

**A** ID 1400 N.W. 62 ST., Ft. Lauderdale, Fl 33309. On-site courses in electronic surveillance, counter measures, video, surveillance optics and covert entry. Law enforcement only.

**American Institute of Applied Science** POB 639 Youngsville, NC 27596. A home study school of forensic science operated by the Sirchie group who also owns LEA and a number of other professional surveillance/investigation aid suppliers. Courses include: Complete Forensic Science Course - Fingerprint Identification, Modus Operandi, Criminal Investigation, Questioned Documents, Firearms Identification, Police Photography. Advanced Forensic Science Course: Fundamentals of Forensic Investigation, Trace Evidence and Its Significance, Fundamentals of Arson and Explosion Investigations, The Significance of Blood in Criminal Investigations, Forensic Investigations Into Drugs and Alcohol, Document and Voice Examination, Firearms, Toolmarks and Footwear Impressions and Investigating Forensic Science on the Internet.

**AT&T**, periodically offers a TSCM school, but you must have a graduate level degree in electrical engineering (or equiv. experience) to get into the class.

**BSF** POB 1302, Moorsville, NC 28115. Brigade Security Forces "The International Combat Academy", neat stuff, courses in counter sniper, executive protection, special response, sub machine gun use, commando operations, escape and evasion, evasive driving, night vision, explosives, covert ops and on and on. BSR3-30 day, on-site courses that use such props as LAW's, Claymores, SMG's and other fun things. Think of it as Club Med for people who like real adventure...

No wind surfing.

**BSR Inc.**, POB 190 Summit Point, WV 25446 www.bsr-inc.com. Law enforcement and emergency driver response schools held at the Summit Point Raceway. Courses include high speed accident avoidance, technical driving, night pursuit, skid control, vehicle dynamics, and some interesting maneuvers conducted under explosive assault or live fire...

They have built an Off-Road Driving Range. Where students are familiarized wtih differnet types of off-road vehicles and receive hands-on training negotiating types of obstacles. These obstacles include steep ascents/descents, rocks, logs, holes, mud, and sand. Students are also familiarized with different recovery techniques.

BSR also offers a one-day Evasive Driver Refresher Course. This includes vehicle dynamics, technical high-speed driving, evasive maneuvers, and simulated attacks.

**The Business Intelligence Institute**, Kirk Tyson International, Chicago World Headquarters, 4343 Commerce Ct., Suite 615, Lisle, IL 60532-3619. Courses offered include: Foundation Skills and Knowledge, Assessing Target

Companies, Networking and Interviewing, Published & On-line Research, Going Deeper Into the Net, BI/CI Management Strategies, International Intelligence, War Rooms and War Gaming, Building a Corporate Intelligence Library, Managing Trade Show Intelligence, Customer Intelligence, Building an Intranet for BI/CI.

**Calibre Press** 666 Dundee Rd., Suite 1607, Northbrook, IL 60062. Street survival seminars for law enforcement.

**Canadian Tactical Defense Institute, Inc.**, 4807 P.S.S.E., Edmonton, Alberta, Canada T5E 5G6. Stress and judgment training for law enforcement.

**Communication Security Inc.**, POB 1815 Bay City, TX 77404. Composed of one Charles Taylor and one Richard Udovich CSI offers a number of services one of which is a unique course scheduled every so often through the auspices of Texas A&M University. This course has a very good reputation as a hands-on look at both sides of the surveillance fence. Rumors have it that the students actually go in the field and work with the real telco equipment.

**DEF-TEC Training Academy** 2399 Forman Rd., Rock Creek, OH 44084. Advanced special weapons and tactics, executive protection, SWAT supervisors course, tactical firearms, chemical munitions instructor certification, Mace/pepper spray instructor certification and several police survival courses.

**Enterprising Securities**, 3336 Montreal Station, Tucker, GA 30084. Enterprising Securities offers the following courses: Maritime Security & Survival for the Protection Specialist; Protection Agent Skills Course for the International Association of Personal Protection Agents; Protective Services Security Advances; Protective Services Counter-Intelligence; Advanced Weapons for the Protection Specialist; Heckler & Koch International Training Division Armorers Course; Oleoresin Capsicum (aka pepper spray) Aerosol Training; Personal Security Awareness and Career Development for the Protection Specialist.

**Executive Protection Institute** Arcadia Manor, Rt. 2, Box 35645, Berryville, PA 22611. Very likely the most famous school of executive protection in the country. Headed by Dr. Richard Kobetz, the staff reads like a Who's Who of ex FBI, CIA, Special Forces, police, professors and government agents in general. This academy has served corporate VIP's celebrities, governors, mayors, military commanders, Presidents, royalty, US Cabinet members and world leaders.Speaks fairly well for the training, wouldn't you agree?

They also do specialized courses in aircraft security, contemporary terrorism, conflict resolution, boat and yacht security, and so on.

**Executive Security International** 2128 Railroad Ave., Suite 206, Rifle, CO 81650. ESI has been teaching courses in executive protection, evasive driving, martial arts and surveillance for the past 12 years. Although I've never attended a course, I have visited the facility and worked with several instructors. They are quite good and bring in visiting experts like John Farnam and Dick Barber for particular courses. Also now offer some home study combined with their resident programs.

**The Final Option** Tactical Force Institute, Inc., POB 378 Mooreton, ND 58061. Law enforcement (or military) only classes in counter sniper ops, riot control, dignitary protection, explosive entry and high risk operations.

**George Washington University** Teaches a series of courses, usually run by the Association of Old Crows.

**G. Gordon Liddy Academy** 800 Brickell Ave., Penthouse Suite, Miami, FL 33131. Courses in "executive protection/electronic counter measures". Learn from a man who was caught during the most famous burglary in the world...

**Global Studies Group, Inc.,** POB 1006, Huntington Beach, CA 92647. www.gsgi.org.

**Global Training Academy Inc.,** POB 445 Somerset, TX 78069. Dog and dog handler training courses for narcotic and explosive detection as well as guard duty.

**Granite Island Group**, James M. Atkinson Granite Island Group 127 Eastern Avenue #291, Gloucester, MA 01931-8008. www.tscm.com. Offers closed enrollment classes for corporate and government clients. TSCM training is geared toward the realistic needs of protective details, full time corporate TSCM teams, and diplomatic details. All training is designed for technical security teams with several years of experience.

Courses available include countermeasures training for vehicles, radiographic inspections, outside/inside plant craft skills, and ESS/PBX analysis.

Students learn the techniques used to locate bugging devices found in computers, workstations, and local area networks. Threat assessment, and intelligence analysis segments of instruction address the issue of developing technologies.

Attendees also learn to program and operate the HP 8560, Tek 490, and RS FSE/FSM series of spectrum analyzers. TSCM gear by Rockwell, Bendix, Thompson, Condor, and Watkins Johnson is also covered.

**H&K International Training Division** 21480 Pacific Blvd., Sterling VA 20166. Heckler & Koch, makers of some of the best firearms available, also offer classes in weapons, tactics, and armorers training. Different locations, different weapons.

**The Information Professionals Institute.** 3724 F.M. 1960 W., Suite 214, Houston, TX 77068. www.ipn.net/ipi. Founded in 1992 by Sue Rugge, Helen

Burwell, and Ruth Orenstein, IPI offers seminars that are distinctly different from the vendor-or data-based specified seminars that are the industry norm. The IPI seminars are designed to offer objective, subject-specific courses which cut across these commercial lines. Continuing education seminars for staff and independent information professionals are offered in major cities throughout the United States each year.

The specific lineup of seminars may vary each year depending on industry developments and the popularity and demand for information on specific topics but IPI wil always offer the latest edition of Sue Rugge's Information Brokers Seminar and Helen Burwell's Public Records Seminar.

**Institute of Public Service** 961 Chesnut St., Gainesville, GA 30501. A well known training institute founded in 1983 to "provide training services and specialized assistance to private and government agencies in 'High Risk Incident Management'". Hands-on courses include anti-terrorism chauffeur driving, crisis management, drug raid operations, executive protection with limited manpower, executive protection (advanced) seminar on terrorism, hostage negotiations, tactical team ops, sniper-counter sniper officer survival and more. Clients include many police departments, major corporations and federal government.

**International Bodyguard Association** Rt.3, Box 639, Brighton, TN 38011. Headed by James King, and ex-special forces, army CID and counterintelligence agent with a Ph.D. in Criminology, M.S. in Forensic Sciences and Bachelor's in Public Administration and Criminal Justice, certified by the FBI in hostage negotiations and licensed as a CPP who has been providing personal protection for US and foreign dignitaries, celebrities and officials since 1967, IBA teaches the fine art of executive protection in seminars offers a home study course, certifies bodyguards and provides a directory of qualified professionals.

**Investigative Training Institute** POB 3379 Annapolis, MD 21403. Beginning and advanced private investigator training programs held on-site by a former State Police Investigator and PI agency owner. Investigation, surveillance, eavesdropping, lie detection, civil procedure, video surveillance and more.

**ISA** 350 Fairfield Ave., Stamford, CT 06902. Workshops on electronic counter measures and electronic security equipment.

**ISG** 239 Longhill Rd., Little Falls, NJ 07024. Law enforcement only courses in telephone systems, surveillance, counter measures and covert entry.

**J. W. Wood & Associates** 4950 W. Dickman Rd., Suite B-4, Battle Creek, MI 49015. A private agency of certified protection specialists who teach special studies in surveillance training, defensive weapons and tactics, executive protection and martial arts for the security professional.

**Jarvis International Intelligence, Inc.,** 11720 21st. St., Tulsa, OK 74129. Eavesdropping counter measures, video operations for everybody; covert entry and surveillance for cops.

**Lion Investigation Academy** 4334 Clearfield St., Freemansburg, PA 18017. A well regarded home study school that specializes in private detective home studies.

**Lockmasters, Inc.,** 5805 Danville Rd., Nicholasville, KY 40356. Serious on -site and home study courses for locksmiths and safe people. Also top end safe gear.

**Mace Security International: Training Division.** POB 679 Bennington, VT 05201. How to Mace someone with flair... (Mace under pressure?).

Oleoresin Capsicum Instructor Course. This one day (8 hour) program is designed to train and certify departmental instructors in the use of Mace brand products for law enforcement and corrections. Course will include dynamic deployment of OC, introduction of the "Tactical L", tactics for surviving an OC attack, ground stabilization concerns, verbalization techniques and field decontamination methods.

**The National Crime Prevention Institute** University of Louisville, Shelby Campus, Burhans Hall, Louisville, KY 40292. Seminars at the "physical security laboratory" located on the Louisville campus, plus on-site courses at other locations. Selections include Crime and Loss Prevention Practice (1 week), Crime and Loss Prevention Management, Crime and Incident Analysis , Prevention and Investigation of Robbery and Burglary, and others.

**National Institute of Bail Enforcement** POB 6757 West Palm Beach, FL 33450. Seminars in bounty hunting and the bail bond business.

**Protective Services Group,** 16161 Ventura Blvd. # 361, Encino, CA 91436-2504. The Executive / VIP Protection Program. Among the subjects covered are; Principles of Protection I, II, III, Risk Assessment, 10-minute Medicine, Advance & Security Surveys, Legal Aspects of Protection, Protective Driving - classroom & track, Assassination Review, Travel - foreign and domestic, Principles of Protective Shooting, Simulated Attack on Principal Training in High Realism Environments, Protective Detail Exercises.

**Quintilian Institute** POB 9351 Arlington, VA 22209. Safe and lock programs that include hands-on training in various aspects of, well, of safes and locks. Designed for security personnel and cops rather than locksmiths.

**RAS – Research Associates of Syracuse, Inc.,** 6780 Northern Blvd., Suite 100, East Syracuse. Courses on Intelligence and TSCM. Most of the training requires a security clearance.

**RENOTT Training & Supplies**. Modern Self Defense for Cops & Civilians. 7237 Serpentine Dr., Dayton, OH 45424. "We aim to teach realistic knife training for both attack and defense. Our clinics will give you some experience at using and defending against a knife. We will be using wood or rubber knives for all attack and defense training.

**Ross Engineering Inc.**, 504 Shaw Rd., #222, Sterling , VA 20166. Courses in eavesdropping detection and prevention as well as shorter, off-site seminars.

**Scars Institute of Combat Sciences** 5230 South 39th St. Phoenix, AZ 85040.

**Sawabini & Associates** 205 Pomander Square, East Aurora, NY 14052. Offers 3-day video camera courses for Law Enforcement. Courses cover how to shoot video for: Accidents, demonstrations, protests, and riots, surveillance & stakeouts, search warrants, asset forfeitures, indoor/outdoor grow operations, drug labs, pre-raid video briefings and gang activities.

Learn to link sound from body-wire to your video camera.

**Special Operations Rescue Tactical Interdiction Expeditions**, SORTIE Publications, 3661P Horseblock Rd, Medford, NY 11763. In a time when water-based rescue technology is rapidly evolving, safety officials need to be updated constantly on new products, procedures and standards. SORTIE meets this urgent need by providing the latest information for all water-based operations.

SORTIE promises to provide public safety officials, police and military personnel with up-to-date information on cutting-edge equipment, training and technology available to assist them in making judgment calls in and out of the theater of operations. By doing this, SORTIE will be promoting the highest of standards.

**Tactical Force Institute**, Tactical Force Institute/TAC-ONE, Inc., 4231 Kodiak, Casper, WY 82604-4403. www.profiles-threat.com. Training offered: SWAT/SRT, Counter Sniper Operations, Crisis Site Management (Command Post), Hostage Rescue, Tactical Movement, Improvised Explosives & Booby-Traps, Police Response to Terrorism, Patrol Response to Critical Incidents, Security Force Evaluation & Training, Dignitary Protection, Major Event Security Planning, Tactical-Medical Urban Survival.

**The Top-Gun Training Center**, The Centurion Group, 1042 N. Mountain Ave. #B-303, Upland, CA 91786. "PISTOLCRAFT 101 a 1-day course which introduces the modern principles of handgun operation, combat targeting, reactive shooting, close-quarters-battle, and evasive movement. PISTOLCRAFT 102; This 2-day course is designed to build your gunhandling skills, marksmanship skills, and tactical skills.

SHOTGUN 104; We cover both the pump and autoloader relative to; Operation, Carry Positions, Deployment, Performance Characteristics, Snap

Shooting, Close & Long Range Applications. Ammo requirement; 250-rnds Trap, 50-rnds #00, 25-rnds Slug&50 rnds pistol. CARBINE 105; This course is designed for semi-auto or selective fire rifles chambered for 9mm to 7.62x39, having iron sights and 20" max. barrel length. The focus is on Gunhandling, CQB and Long Range Applications, and Ballistic Performance".

**Universal Propulsion Company** 25401 North Central Ave., Phoenix, AZ 85027-7899. www.upco-inc.com. Universal Propulsion Company offers a full range of tactical training. Subjects include: SWAT/SRT, Counter Sniper Operations, Command Post Operations, Improvised Explosive Devices, Counter Terrorism in Law Enforcement, Tactical-Medical Urban Survival, Patrol Response to Crisis Incidents, Hostage Rescue.

# SAMPLE NEWSLETTER
## Ordering Details On Last Page

# How To Get Anything On Anybody—*The Newsletter*

## Investigative Techniques • Surveillance • Counter Surveillance • Information Tracking and Privacy

Volume 1 — Sample • A Publication of Intelligence Incorporated • 3555 S. El Camino Real #309 • San Mateo, CA 94403 • Subscriptions $109/year

# ULTIMATE WEAPON?

How To Get Anything On Anybody—*The Newsletter* may just be the most unusual newsletter ever pubished, but the first time it saves you several hundred dollars on an equipment purchase, provides the exact source for that unlisted phone number, hidden bank account, pager record or just puts you directly on the track of that skip who has gone to ground you'll think it may just be the best newsletter in the world...

*"Dear Mr. Lapin, I have mixed emotions about your letter, I love getting each issue but I really hesitate to talk it up because I don't want my competiton to know how to get the same secrets"*—D.R State Investigator, Illnois.

This special issue is a sample of our newsletter, it contains summaries of a few of the hard and fast articles our readers love.

INVESTIGATIVE TECHNIQUES, SURVEILLANCE, COUNTER SURVEILLANCE, INFORMATION TRACKING AND PRIVACY

*For the first time ever* the latest techniques, tricks, products and opportunities laid out in a single newsletter! Written/edited by Lee Lapin (author; The Whole Spy Catalog, How To Get Anything On Anybody; Books I and II, The Covert Catalog, Hands-On Surveillance, etc.) *How To Get Anything On Anybody—The Newsletter* is the only periodical to feature Lee's unique, hard and fast, chocked-full-of-information style.

**PEOPLE TRACKING, ASSET SEARCHING BREAKTHROUGHS**—Newest, best, most complete databases/search services, getting around "we can't give you that information" restrictions. Newest tricks for locating bank accounts, running down credit card purchase records, *a source for pager records.* **SURVEILLANCE, COUNTER SURVEILLANCE.** Tests/sources for bloody amazing GPS trackers, video pagers, watches, sunglasses. Newest/best

surveillance gear/dealers. How to improvise surveillance devices from available products. A new company that will rent *you* the latest in electronic surveillance and countermeasures gear. **BUSINESS INTELLIGENCE**—Keep up with the Kompetition: Databases, search sources, methodology, people. places and guns for hire. **PRIVACY? TRUTH IN BANKING?** Why the new US currency can be more dangerous to your health then any other financial transaction. How to protect yourself from unnecessary investigations and audits. Offshore havens that are still secure, asset hiding services, do they provide real asset protection? Cutting edge info on ID scams, verification methods, cross-checking, passport alternatives, plus social security fraud trackers, "hawk" accounts, and how the Big Three credit bureaus are digging out secondary, trick and questionable accounts. **INTERROGATING THE INTERNET**—Little known sources to password cracking programs.

Too time sensitive for a book, *How To Get Anything On Anybody—The Newsletter* will pay for itself the first time you track down a "ghost", dig out "hidden" information, protect a bank account, or just give golden advice to a client. **HTGAOA-TN** will stun you with professional secrets, tricks of the trade, "inside" phone numbers, ordering information, plus cutting edge techniques to trace, track, surveil and investigate anyone or anything...

- 8 pages per issue, mailed first class 10 times a year. Satisfaction guaranteed? Of course it is, cancel at any time and Intelligence Incorporated will refund the remainder of your subscription price. $109.00 per year ($129.00 foreign)

## People Tracking Extraordinary

Some of you make a living at this (as I have), some just have an occasional need, (PI's, cops, debt chasers), and once in a while everyone wakes up

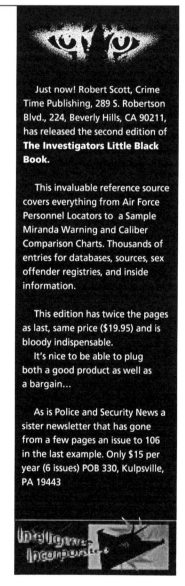

# How To Get Anything On Anybody—*The Newsletter*

The first listing is valuable both for competitive intelligence projects as well as people tracking/credit reporting. **EDGAR** (Electronic Data Gathering, Analysis, and Retrieval) is a database operated by the Securities and Exchange Commission.

One can search the base by company name at www.sec.gov/cgi-bin/srch-edgar. Results include a wealth of information on any company which files with the SEC.

Other web sites of interest: sunsite.unc.edu/~masha/ How to find e-mail addresses www.qucis.queen.ca/FAQa/ email/finding.html E-mail search site

laying next to the wife of 22 years, rolls over in bed and just wonders what the hell ever happened to that girl he took to the junior prom.

The art of People Tracking, and I say art instead of science for a reason, is an example of a practice that combines the complexities of a New York Times crossword puzzle with the difficulties of an Apollo space launch.

You gotta consider the path, price versus probability, choosing the correct databases, the correct search strings, who(m) you can pretext, and the routes less chosen…

Let's start with one of the latter today—

Targets, i.e., people being searched for, may be lost due to any number of reasons, overlooked, forgotten or deliberately hiding. You can guess which are the most difficult to find…

So, you, as a diligent searcher have run a credit header search, done the various phone disc's, maybe a specialty report or two.

Stop and think about it for a minute, if you are a deliberate "skip" how recent, how good do you figure your credit header (or credit report) is going to be?

Keep up the payments on the old VISA card? Sure. Report your change of address to the post office? Of course you would. Pass on that new address to the bank, sleazy car lot, various collections agencies, IRS, fill out those change of address forms?

Hell, yes, after all you're a citizen, right?

Well bunky, some people are not as religiously oriented as you were brought up to be and some not only forget these tiny social obligations, some actually lie their asses off…

So where do you look for those crack slippers?

**Tele-Track**
**3841 Holcomb Bridge Rd.**
**Norcross, GA 30092**

Has put together a new type of credit database. They perform several services, most aimed at merchants who don't want to see that "return to maker" stamp on the check.

If an individual attempts to purchase a certain type of merchandise from more than one retailer within 60 days (why would you need 5 couches and 14 TV's in 60 days?) they are flagged, the file comes up and TT members are notified.

This service is called Skipguard and will provide the exact reasons the alert was flagged plus all known information on the individual.

**Now For The Good Stuff**: TT has also discovered a market for tracing "sub-prime" creditors (i.e., scum, flakes, sleeaze, whatever).

"Tele-Track is in the sub-prime consumer information business. We collect and report information to and from merchants who interface with high risk consumers daily, including rent-to-own stores, sub-prime furniture and appliance stores, sub-prime consumer finance companies, sub-prime auto dealers, finance companies, sub-prime mortgage companies, check advances/deferred deposit/loan companies and cable TV companies."

Unlike consumer reporting agencies TT's database contains only negative information. Basically it tracks those nice folks that have to use check cashing agencies, rent their coffee tables and $70 stereos for $43.00 a month, skip on rental agreements, bounce checks, or wander off with non-fully paid automobiles.

Hey, maybe just the type of person you might be looking for…

MergeHit is another service that will automatically search for any other entries using the same SS number over the past 30 days *as well as* keep watching for additional entries forever.

When a match is found the merchant reporting the new (or at least recent) entry is contacted and all available information about the individual is assembled and then forwarded by TT.

MergeHit reports typically contain –
- Name and SS number of account
- Date of entry as well as address, phone number of merchant involved
- Items charged
- All available info on the account including name, phone #'s, addresses and reported employer
- Name address and phone of the merchant who most recently inquired about that account
- A list of past entries and inquiries from TT's database which can point to a pattern of movement

This is an invaluable service as the information is often *minutes* old…

Several new sources have appeared on the horizon recently that offer some real possibilities for tracking and backgrounding. The most interesting is probably a company called:

**Advanced Research**
**POB 195**
**Parsippany, NJ 07054**
**www.advsearch.com**

AR offers some very difficult to come by information, and more importantly they offer much of it on a no hit—no charge basis. This system offers the ultimate guarantee for any information broker.

# How To Get Anything On Anybody—*The Newsletter*

If you don't get the information requested you don't pay anything. Sounds logical, but is rather difficult to find in real life. It's easy to advertise unlisted phone numbers, toll records, credit card reports, charge an outrageous fee and then find some excuse for not providing the information.

Highlights of AR's offerings include:

- Phone Number trace. published or unpublished, track to owner, provide name and address. 800 and 900's okay NO HIT – NO CHARGE
- Beeper trace. Name and address of pager owner. NHNC
- Cell Phone Trace same as above. NHNC
- Disconnected number trace. Name address of former owner forwarding info if at all possible NHNC
- Cellular call records. List of all calls made from a particular phone. NHNC
- Regional bank account locator. NHNC

Other services offered on a pay basis (but covered by a very comprehensive warranty that includes money back for incorrect information) include: National bank account locator, phone toll records, safe deposit box search and credit card activity.

## 30 Ways To Find Someone's Social Security Number

As most of you realize the key to getting any information on an individual from a skip trace, credit header search, asset location procedure, or background investigation is the individual's unique US ID card, better known as the social security card.

The following is a list supplied by Joe Dickerson and used with his permission. It is not meant to be 100% complete but should provide some food for thought.

1. Driver's license application
2. Voter's registration application.
3. Professional license application.
4. Bankruptcy file
5. Income statement from divorce/settlement file
6. Financial statements
7. Tax returns
8. Credit report
9. Tax lien filings
10. Deposition
11. Interrogatories
12. UCC records
13. Limited partnership filings
14. Credit/loan applications
15. Insurance applications
16. Bank files
17. Employment applications
18. Resume
19. School records
20. Military records
21. Medical records
22. Marriage license applications
23. Loan/rental application
24. Criminal records
25. Telephone application
26. Utility application
27. Pilot license application
28. Hunting fishing license application
29. FCC radio license
30. Death certificate

Inmate Locator Line
Public Information, Bureau of Prisons
UD Department of Justice
320 First st, NW Rm 640
Wasington, DC 20536
202-307-3198

This department exists to locate persons ("loved one's") who might be incarcerated in local, state of federal correction institutions. They also maintain a "hot line" known as the Inmate Locator Line 202-307-3126 10 a.m. — 4:30 p.m. EST.

Military Service Branch National Archives and Records Administration
8th St. and Pennsylvania Ave NW, Room 13W
Washington, DC 20408
202-501-5385

This clearinghouse holds records of military personnel separated from the Air Force, Army, Navy, Marine Corps, Coast Guard, Confederate States volunteers as well as veteran's records.

They publish a $2.00 booklet that provides details about their holdings and records.

Need an information broker to run a search on a person or dig up some desperate data? Besides the usual printed lists (Whole Spy Catalog, Burwell Guide) an on-line non-profit resource composed of IB's and associates (the latter being involved in the field in some way) can be found at:

Association of Independent Information Professionals
234 W. Delaware Ave
Pennington, NJ 08534
609-730-8469 (fax)
73263.34@compuserve.com

Over the past few years a bunch of firms have specialized in the collection and dissemination of "tenant" data for perspective land-

A relatively new service from, of all people, AT&T is very useful when people tracking – 1-900-555-1212 will look up any name on a nationwide basis. They will find the correct area code, consult local directory assistance and if a non-pub is located they will automatically search old directories for a published version of the same person.

Two look ups per call, under a buck per call...

# How To Get Anything On Anybody—*The Newsletter*

## Best phone/address database?

**www.AnyWho.com.** offers a free (as of now) service that has received rave reviews in a number of publications that should know.

An advanced World Wide Web-based directory service site, AnyWho Directory Service, integrates traditional business and consumer white and yellow pages telephone listings with enhanced, Internet-based contact information such as E-mail Addresses and Web Site URLs. Toll Free and FAX numbers.

Created by the Internet Directory Group of AT&T Labs, AnyWho makes its living by adding a touch of advertising to the basic services offered, is no doubt collecting names for a marketing effort or two (yes, expect it to attempt to send a cookie or two).

AnyWho also allows businesses to add information to AnyWho, expanding their coverage by voluntary contribution.

AnyWho demonstrates some of the fastest search response times on the web and "features web pages designed to provide consumers with quick, easy-to-use access to business information over dial-up Internet connections".

One can search by a variety of criteria including business category, name, city, and state.

Business listings attempt to include enhanced information (Web Site URL, E-mail Address, FAX, and/or Toll Free Number) for a one stop shopping experience.

AnyWho allows one to perform a single search across multiple directories to find traditional and enhanced business listing information as well as conventional people tracking.

It also features a nice reverse 800# feature.

All contact information is combined into a single listing. AnyWho features over 90 million consumer and over 10 million business listings as well as offering a map call up service and driving instructions to many of the listed businesses.

lords. Normally the would-be landlord joined one or more associations and then paid a per search fee to see if that particular organization had any records of interest.

Now Trans Resigtry Limited is an automated search engine that links about 200 courthouses across the nation for landlord-tenant court records (as well as credit reports, private tenant records, skip tracing and other searches designed for people who manage property *but* can work well for many other uses).

**Trans Registry Limited**
**11140 Rockville Pike #1200**
**Rockville, MD 20852**

A target's earning history cannot be gotten directly from the SSA but can be gotten from the following company *with the subject's permission.*

**Edge Information Service Management, Inc.**
**One Harbor Place**
**1901 South Harbor Blvd. Ste. 401**
**Melbourne, FL 32901**
**800 780-3299 (fax)**

One of the most frustrating dead ends in skip or asset searching is to run into the Post Office box, or mail drop.

Yes, here is my DMV address, my tag registration, I get all my checks, bills, and magazines at my primary address. It just happens to be a 6" x 6" domicile. I live cheap.

How can you run down a box owner's real address, dig the same info out of Mail Boxes R Us, or find a real forwarding address?

Copy the following Request For Change Of Address or Boxholder Information Needed for Service of Legal Process onto your own letterhead (actual form on page 8). Note this form has already had an important modification added from the government original. The line "person still receives mail at this address is a creative addition that will filled in about 50% of the time".

- Address the form to the postmaster of the town where the box or former address is located.
- Turn it in to your friendly postal clerk.
- UNDER COURT AND DOCUMENT INFO write the word pending. A. It probably is pending. B. No PO anywhere in the world with the exception of one minor incident in upper Senegal, has ever taken the time to see if any court action is, indeed, pending.
- **Result** – you should be given boxholder s real address or forwarding address.
- **Result** – Clerk decides you are an idiot or has never heard of this form.

- Politely (always be polite) ask for the supervisor, show documents
- **Result** –You get it or you get nada. If nada politely ask for postal inspector's phone number repeat process adding a reference to postal relegation 352.44 (and addendums) which state the conditions under which the post office must release this information.

Should end here, but if boxholder's real address turns out to be a vacant lot or the Bank of America Building, you can legally request that his mail be held and not put into his box until he has filled out a new and updated residence card.

This card is supposed to be verified by the carrier on the route. Sometimes they will do this, sometimes it takes a bit more gentle persuasion.

Private mail drops have to conform to this exact same set of regulations. Forget the phone, walk in with your nicely printed form and ask for the info. When they refuse ask if you can borrow their phone to call the local postal inspector.

Pretex—Ain't going to work on a major city dealing with a jaded clerk, but might in a small town, bored PM or a private drop clerk.

Call, or better yet show up in person decked out in a UPS/Fed Ex uniform with a package under your arm from Computer's R Us. You have an overnight delivery for Dennis Rodman at this address. You assume he did leave the certified check for $4312.09. Correct? No?

What do you mean no? Man paid $57 for overnight delivery, said he would leave check with you. Damnit all anyway, tomorrow is James Dean, patron Saint of all delivery drivers birthday and it's a holiday.

Do you happen to have a phone number or address where I can deliver this turkey today, after all he paid us for overnight service?

## Better Living Thru Electronics
### Computer and Email Security

Although not designed to be a complete text on computer snooping/hacking/protecting this letter will from time to time concentrate on things that you really should know about those machines that have taken over our lives.

The first item on this month's agenda is what do you, or a corporate spy, cop or government agent do when you have access to someone's computer.

If you are the agent or cop-with-a-warrant, you take it away.

4

# How To Get Anything On Anybody—*The Newsletter*

At once. Ask Monica Lewnisky what was the first thing was they grabbed from her...

Then you start playing around with the data. Data that is in the clear is in the clear. Read it, copy it. Go look at the cache or recently-looked-at documents file to see exactly what web sites the target has been visiting.

Yes they are all recorded there until the RAM becomes full.

If the files are encrypted, you got a problem pal. PGP is pretty hard to crack. According to sources which I cannot name and not expect the dreaded knock, a one time run through on PGP protects you from anybody but the feds.

Run the same material thru twice and you have now moved into the area of the NSA or nobody...

But even if some material is encrypted you have some other possibilities. Many people still do not realize that when you "erase" a file from one of your drives the file is not *deleted!*

All the computer does is change the pointer; i.e., the designator in front of the file to one that says, "I'm really not needed so once you run out of hard disk space you can write on top me. Otherwise leave me alone." On IBM this designator is 229.

The first thing one would do to recover this "trashed" data would be to run a copy of Norton Utilities tool called Unerase.This will bring back most data.

Now suppose you have typed some really sensitive data on a particular computer or disc and some careless son-of-a-bitch, perhaps your maid, tosses out the only copy of your password with the six month old dog food can you had it carefully noted on.

Your only copy.

Now, of course, knowing my readers, I realize none of you would consider using this procedure on someone else's programs that so I have no second thoughts about passing on a new company of now-legit hackers called Crak Software, whose very motto is "You Hack 'em, we Crack 'em."

According to John Kuslich (head geek what's in charge) Crak will recover lost passwords so you can access your data on damn near every word processor and spreadsheet program around. So if you ve got this encrypted file that is just screaming for a clear read?

Fax Crak at 602-548-1993 or visit their site at www.crak.com where you can down load sample (demo) programs and then give them a call for the security code to enable the software.

Victims, ah, rather potential targets include files encrypted in Word, Excel, Lotus, QuattroPro, WordPerfect, Quicken, Corel, Windows 95/NT, and so on.

Step two is to send the disk (hard or floppy) to a specialized recovery company such as ONTRACK (Minneapolis). They can often bring back not only the not-really-deleted-data but sometimes data that has actually been written over once.

Even if you were able to ensure that your hard-drive files would be overwritten each time you deleted a file, you could still be vulnerable. There are copies of the deleted files you may not know about. Operating systems like Windows 95 and software programs like Excel also make extra copies in addition to the one you think you just deleted.

Any Windows swap file, which provides temporary data storage, may retain copies of secret passwords and critical data. In addition, your Internet browser's cache and history files paint a vivid picture of your World Wide Web browsing habits.

Even if you use good encryption you must realize when you encrypt a file, your encryption program should overwrite the original, unencrypted version of that file. Unfortunately, each time you create a file (with programs such as Microsoft Word or Lotus 1-2-3), your program may create additional, temporary copies of your files on the hard disk.

Even though the original file may be overwritten and encrypted, these temporary copies are not. A hex editor or undelete program can be employed to retrieve these temporary files and view the sensitive data that you thought was safely encrypted.

In summary, most encryption programs protect only the final version of a document, but ignore copies that word-processors make in the course of copying, saving and manipulating files. These copies are apparently deleted, but can hang around on the hard disk until actively overwritten with other data. Even if a file is overwritten, it can often be recovered by taking the disk apart and examining its magnetic history.

So what to do? Two things:

Encrypt everything with a good program and then look into a new program called:

Shredder
Stratfor Co
3301 Northland Drive, Suite 500
Austin, TX 78731
email: info@shredder.com

Another way to quickly return an IP address from a domain name is to use NetScan Tools, a shareware program (free for 30 days, then $25 for ownership license) which runs with Windows 95.

It's a straightforward useful program and can be found at: www.eskimo.com/~nwps/index.html.

The ultimate privacy invasion? The IRS, yes your *IRS*, now provides tax return data to mortgage lenders. This, ah, somewhat synergistic relationship works for everybody. Buy a house, state your income at $80K to help qualify the loan, file $23K on your tax return and, trust me on this, you will be talking to both the lender and a pleasant IRS field agent before any money changes hands.

# How To Get Anything On Anybody—*The Newsletter*

## Deal Of The Month

Or, in this case, maybe the decade:

Ever wonder what messages your competitor, high school aged kid, wife, or the 22 year old guy next door who drives a BMW and has no job is getting on that little belt-clipped pager he's never without?

Popular Electronics, March 1997 has a great article on how to build a pager decoder. This device interfaces a scanner type receiver with your laptop in order to grab all the pager messages transmitted by any particular paging company.

Not only does it log and display any/all messages, you can, as PE says, "keep a log of your own messages so you don't miss any", by pre-programming the unit to only record messages to any individual pager.

This unit not only logs numeric messages but most of the popular alpha-numeric signals as well.

In the past I've reviewed several commercial software/hardware systems that do exactly this same thing, and do it well.

Best system about $4,000, low end, law enforcement oriented pager grabbers?

About $2,000.

PE's unit can be purchased in kit form for $65.00 including all parts, circuit board, case and a free copy of the AccuPage Radio Monitor Program.

$79.95, demo can be down loaded at their web site www.shredder.com

What does Shredder do? It automatically overwrites any data you instruct it to up to 12 times (depending on the level of protection needed) with meaningless 1's and 0's.

Over writes it 12 times...

Shredder comes with five levels of security depending on your situation. Level five takes into account that NSA's electron microscopes with spin detectors that can ferret out small bits of characters that differ by as little as 1/1000 of a millimeter.

Lastly, but not leastly, there is the "Shredisk" command which kisses off all the information on your drive for ever and ever and ever.

Don't use this program while drinking or abusing drugs. Your drive will not live to regret it.

## Covert Video

The Sony EVO 220 is the heart and soul of most covert video operations. Coupled with its Z-Box Event Recorder (see issue 1) the 220 can be programmed to turn on at specific signals, run for so long, turn off, as well as more tricks than my pet wolf knows.

The 220 has been strapped to more bodies than the cross-my-heart-bra for covert "sting" type operations from drug buys to bribing senators. Coupled with a hidden camera it does a fine job of recording most close-in, nefarious transactions.

The system does have a few shortfalls – most pager/tie/sunglass cameras run from their own power sources and the 220 from another. There's really no way to tell if the unit is actually recording, power sources run down at different intervals, etc.

**ISIS Investigations, Inc.,**
**427 S Vine st**
**Tyler TX 75702**

is an investigative agency that has utilized the Sony system in a variety of different operations. They grew tired of the shortcomings and had their in-house engineer design a small interface box that works with modified 220's to solve many potential problems.

Their box converts the 220 battery voltage to allow operation of most mini cameras (pagers, etc.) from the 220's own power supply. The interface also includes an auto gain audio amplifier which improves the sound quality measurably as well as a lighted remote on/off

switch that controls both the camera and the recorder.

Stash the 220 in a fanny pack, purse, strapped to your body, run the camera wires to the interface, put the control switch in a comfortable position and hit it...

Waiting for a dishonest waiter or drug dealer to come back from his contact? Turn the machine off with a touch of the switch, don't waste tape filming the envirnoment. If you place the switch where you can see the red glow you always know when you are actually recording.

ISIS sells the entire package including a pager cam and modified 220 or will modify yours for a fee.

A really cheap/neat piece of software has just come on the market. Called **DigitalRadar** and made by Connectix, it equips any computer that has a tethered digital camera with an automatic motion sensor.

The program can be set up for automatic operation with a movement threshold defined. Anytime movement is detected by the camera (i.e., someone enters the area) the computer records all activity and saves the images as either still or video in a file you can open and browse when you return.

The obvious use to is to see who enters your office/workplace when you are not around and exactly what they do.

Great way to catch thieves, people browsing thru your computer files when you are not around or just see what s going on in any area where you keep a computer.

Or can move a computer to; say a bedroom perhaps?

If you already own the hardware the program will set you back a whole $30. A bit cheaper than buying a pinhole camera and time lapse recorder. DR is available from any of the major computer suppliers, or you can visit the connectix.com web page.

## How To Follow Anyone Anywhere — Better Living Thru Electronics...

Okay, suppose you want to follow any vehicle, anywhere in the world, in real time from the comfort of your office/living room/favorite bar...

Right out of James Bond, huh?

Or maybe you just want to know where a particular vehicle has been over the last several days. I mean, exactly where it has traveled, stopped, stayed (and for how long), speed involved and roads traveled...

# How To Get Anything On Anybody—*The Newsletter*

Because the GPS receiver actually compares the time of the transmission versus its reception it actually works more like radar than normal radio direction finding gear.

The GPS system sends two separate signals: a Standard Positioning Service (SPS) for civilians and a Precise Positioning Service Signal (PPS) for the military.

The former system has an inbred accuracy of about 25 meters 95% of the time. This Circle Error Probable is a deliberate effort by the defense department to limit the accuracy of anybody else's cruise missiles...

The military signal provides accuracy down to a few feet.

Selective Availability (SA) degrades the civilian system by introducing a "dither" on the time signal so that terrorists, bill collectors and lawyers cannot get the same accuracy as our armed services.

Some organizations, notably the Coast Guard and upper crusty country clubs offer GPS accuracy down to well under 10 feet. They do this by picking a single location (country clubs traditionally utilize the caddie shack), establish its *precise* location and then broadcast a separate FM signal to specially equipped receivers that corrects the on-purpose inaccuracy of the civilian GPS signal.

If you can't follow a vehicle within a 25 meter error factor I suggest you go back into that Burger King manager training program and learn to love those fries brown...

## Active GPS

In which, you, the investigator, clamps a magnetic leech transmitter on the underside of the target vehicle. A thin wire connects a high gain antenna which you place under the rubber/plastic bumper of any modern vehicle.

The high gain antenna will see thru the material and grab 3 GPS satellites *in most areas.*

Our friends in the FBI have a really great system. The main problems inherent in GPS tracking are: Hiding the unit, seeing the satellites and an adequate power supply.

The Feebies, who are going to write me thank you notes for sharing this with you, normally operate with an amazing tool not all of us have.

It's a small piece of paper with the word "warrant" prominently displayed. This means they can do "black" installs.

Routinely this includes opening the target vehicle, hard wiring the transmitter to the onboard power supply, stashing the unit, often in the trunk under the spare tire and then run-

ning the antenna(s) up directly under the rear trunk cover or compartment lid.

Most modern vehicles have two or more nice, symmetrical holes cut thru the metal lid for the placement of stereo speakers. Holes only covered by carpet that look right up thru the rear window...

Nice, right? Endless power, hidden *inside* the vehicle and a clear shot at the positioning satellites.

That's why they get the big bucks...

### Rent To Own

The GPS System is so slick, clever surveillance oriented businessmen are already offering alternatives.

**StarTrac, Inc.**
**3575 Beltline Road**
**Suite 347**
**Irving, TX**

Offers a lease-rent-purchase option on a covert GPS system, in most parts of the US.

Utilizing approximately the same sized unit, same accuracy as the II and Shadow, one rents the actual equipment and then simply calls into the nice people at StarTrac to set up the service requirements, which can include on-demand locating, automatic notification, real time surveillance, notify client when vehicle reaches or leaves a particular target area and so on.

### Electronic Surveillance

Crem of da la crem! 10 days ago the annual National Technical Investigator's Association show/seminar was held in Phoenix, Arizona. This yearly get together brings the world's best surveillance equipment manufacturers/dealers and their potential customers face to face in order to examine the latest surveillance/counter equipment and techniques.

This gathering is closed to everyone except government surveillance investigators and technicians. Most of the equipment is title 3 and/or classified, not available to anyone that be not in the employ of Uncle Sam.

Even the exhibitors are, for the most part, low key, slash, unheard of by those in the private sector. Virtually every heavy hitter in the industry with exception of the CIA and FBI's own private labs, trot out their latest offerings at this 6 day show.

Now, for the sake of an interesting conversational topic, say that you have a friend in the biz, maybe your uncle.

Maybe Uncle Lee...

Think electronic surveillance is fading from the scene? The FBI wants Congress to release $2 *billion* to upgrade their wiretapping capabilities to keep abreast of the telco's switch to digital phone systems. They also want some 50,000 warrants this year and have admitted to tapping more than 1,000 lines in the city of Los Angeles per *day.*

How To Get Anything On Anybody—*The Newsletter*

**Intelligence Incorporated**
**3555 S. El Camino Real #309**
**San Mateo, CA 94403**

# First Class Mail

Lee Lapin's *How To Get Anything On Anybody—The Newsletter* is published 10 times a year by Intelligence Incorporated. Information contained herein is obtained from sources believed to be reliable, but accuracy cannot be guaranteed. Intelligence Incorporated and its officers and editors do not have any financial interest in any products or services listed in *How To Get Anything On Anybody—The Newsletter* unless otherwise noted.

All information is presented with the understanding that certain techniques and equipment may be illegal in some applications and/or some geographical locations.

Intelligence Inc. and its officers, editors and Lee Lapin take no responsibility for misuse of any information included. It is the sole responsibility of each reader to determine legality of any particular technique or equipment and to act within the laws governing such information.

No more than 250 words of this newsletter may be reproduced or extracted in context without permission of the publisher.

Copyright 1998 Lee Lapin.

Please address all correspondence, subscription and editorial inquiries to Intelligence Incorporated, 3555 S. El Camino Real, #309, San Mateo, CA 94403.

Subscriptions $109.00 per year or $189 for two years.

## IN UPCOMING ISSUES

### Upcoming in *How To Get Anything On Anybody–The Newsletter*:

Asset searching revisited, "secret" people tracking sources, smart cards, electronic wallets, finding/protecting safe deposit boxes, tests of the best civilian bugs still available, new surveillance sources, "white stenos"—the ultimate way to transmit private information, glyphs—watch while a top secret Xerox project transforms information protection and dispersal in a format borrowed from the Incas, book reviews, information provider bench tests, the ultimate computer "theft" program and where to get it, how to steal email and much more!

Plus upcoming courses, seminars, shows the hottest new web sites, best databanks, new equipment and information suppliers.

**Stay On The Fast Track!! Subscribe Today!**
**Mail or fax the subscription form, or order online at**
**our website, and you won't miss a single issue.**

# MISCELLANEOUS
## And Too Late To Classify

# The Occasional Swimmer's Kit

Install any portable radio — with antenna attached — inside a soft, padded nylon container. Strap the headset to your head and the container to your body — and go swimming — the entire kit is **submersible in saltwater** — some versions are submersible to 66 feet

For portable radio users who need to operate radios in... on... or under water

**Headset**
held securely in place with elastic strap, fabric headband and touch fastener

**Earphone**
fits under most helmets —
has soft attenuation earcup to aid hearing in high noise

**Boom mic or throat mic**

**Press-to-talk switch**
— see options below

**Radio container**
accommodates any portable radio with antenna attached mount on belt, back or chest

**Television Equipment Associates, Inc.,** Box 393 South Salem, NY 10590.
Okay, now you are sunning on the family yacht when suddenly you glance over the side and lo and behold, the most gorgeous female you've ever seen is tangled in the anchor chain 22 feet below the surface.

Crying for help. Desperate. Quickly you grab your Occasional Swimmer's Kit, throw it on and jump in the water. As you lock lips and fill her lungs with a life giving breath you pause, pick up the microphone and call the nearest hotel to reserve the honeymoon suite for the night...

For boaters, windsurfers and swimmers who need to keep in touch. Use your favorite walkie talkie from 66 feet down. Who was this designed for?

Can you say the word, "seals?"

**Stinger Spike Systems Inc.**, POB 8484 Monticello, UT 84535. The photo pretty much explains the function. For those with the need for less stopping power Shomer-Tec sells single spikes.

**Incredible Adventures** 6604 Midnight Pass Rd., Sarasota FL 34242 www.incredible-adventures.com. You have been selected for an ultra-secret paramilitary unit for a covert mission in hostile terrotority. Only the best trained agents will be able to survive the mission, so your training must be thorough and intense. You will be taken to a secret training base where a hand picked cadre of Green Berets and contract mercs from the world's toughest groups will teach you all the skills you need from evasive driving to placing explosives and booby-traps."

Child care is available...

## HELPING THE WORLD COMMUNICATE WITH WIRELESS PHONE, FAX AND DATA WHERE CELLULAR IS NOT NECESSARY AND PHONE LINES ARE NOT AVAILABLE

### CUSTOM SYSTEMS ARE AVAILABLE....
### ....JUST TELL US WHAT YOU NEED.

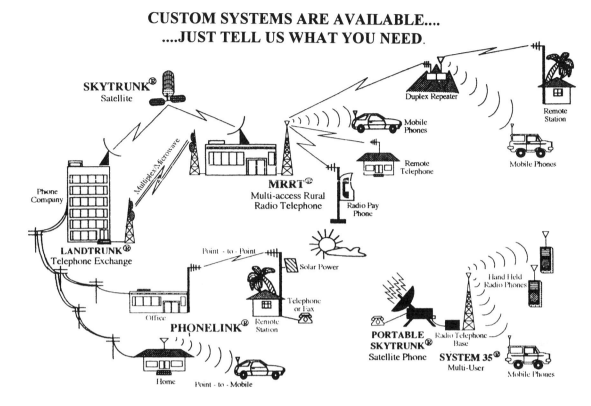

**Telemobile Wireless Communications Systems** 19840 Hamilton Ave., Torrance, CA 90502 www.telemobile.com. For 35 years TM has been one of the world leaders in point-point communications systems for both voice and data. Handheld 2 ways, mobile and permanent transceivers. Units can be ordered in UHF or VHF with or without scrambling.

Also some nice briefcase mounted repeaters.

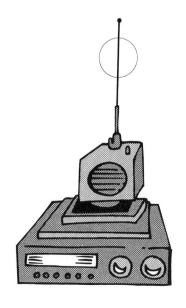

**Atlantic Ham Radio Ltd.,** 368 Wilson Ave., Toronto, Ont. M3H 1S9 Canada www.interlog.com/~ahr/ scan.html. 800 MHz two way radios plus a couple of AOR/ICOM scanners at very good prices.

**The Electronic Goldmine** POB 5408 Scottsdale, AZ 85261. A supplier of electronic components including miniature microphone elements and various telephone parts. They also carry a few items of interest to those in the surveillance community.

You will *not* beat their prices...

# GEOSOURCE GEOPHONE

Very unique vibration detector made for geologists to detect oil-bearing underground faults. These can detect footsteps up to 50 feet away. Possible uses include making homemade seismographs, people/animal remote detectors, burglar alarms, etc. Rating listed on the side of the 1 1/4" tall x 1" dia. sealed unit is 14 Hz, 325 ohm. We supply a circuit diagram that shows how to use a couple of resistors, a trimpot, a LED, a LM 393 IC, and a 9V battery to make an extremely sensitive vibration detector. These unusual scientific devices are brand new.

## $8.95

# 900 MHZ WIRELESS VIDEO RECEIVER

Brand new 900 MHZ wireless video receiver made by Private Eye Surveillance Co. This receiver is able to receive 900 MHZ video signals from various models of 900 MHZ wireless TV cameras. The signal is then converted to a standard black & white signal so you don't need to use a monitor. Works with black & white or color TV. Works on ch3 or ch4 and features operation from a small AC adapter (included), red on indicator, tuning control, antenna, TV/wireless switch, connection cable to hookup to your TV "in" jack. Has a "DIN" connector on back of unit to use with a monitor (if desired) and audio and video RCA jacks to use with a monitor (if desired). Can work with VCR's to record video from your surveillance camera. The only thing you need to provide is the TV and a 900 MHZ wireless TV camera.

**G8914**

## $19.95

**OmiGlow** 96 Windsor Street, West Springfield, MA 01089 www.omniglow.com. Cyalume light stick (chemical illumination) in a variety of shapes and sizes, but the coolest entry is called the Flashstick.

Crack it open, shake it and a "blinding" light floods the scene for the next two minutes.

**DynaMetric, Inc.,** 717 South Myrtle Ave., Monrovia, CA 91016 www.dynametric.com. Not engineered with surveillance types in the for front, DM makes a number of cute direct telephone record interfaces that meet and beat a variety of applications (beep, no beep, plug adapters) for us interested parties.

Once again, pieces sold by many other dealers. Buy from the source.

| Model | Features | 2-Prong/Modular | Continuous Record | Auto Shut-Off* | Power |
|-------|----------|-----------------|-------------------|----------------|-------|
| THP-702L | Basic Unit | 2-Prong | ✔ | – | none |
| THP-734SY | Amplified recorder output | both | ✔ | – | 6VDC |
| THP-737SY | Amplified output, beeps | both | ✔ | – | 6VDC |
| THP-700LM* | Basic Unit, no beeps | both | – | ✔ | 9VDC |
| THP-700L* | Beeps | both | – | ✔ | 9VDC |
| THP-700MSY* | No beeps, amplified output | both | – | ✔ | 9VDC |
| THP-700SY* | Beeps, amplified output | both | – | ✔ | 9VDC |

**Hitek International** 484 El Camino Real, Redwood City, CA 94063. Has just announced the release of a new night vision device which they promise is "the most inexpensive" such unit on the market.

The Flea uses non-milspec tubes – Hitek purchases their intensifier tubes directly from the military, purchasing those which did not live up to the exact specifications required for Uncle Sam.

Basically each unit is a second, the tube may have tiny dark and/or light spots which disqualifies them for military units but they are still very usable for us civilians.

Made in the U.S.A., with a choice between 2nd and 3rd gen., and powerful IR illuminator for use even in complete darkness, the little Flea will leap over any big night vision device on today's market. It is <u>guaranteed</u> to be the most inexpensive high performance night vision unit ever made.

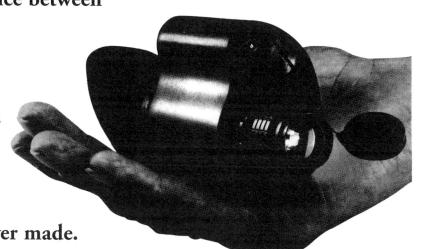

**Moonlight Products** 10401 Roselle Street, San Diego, CA 92121 www.moonlightproducts.com. Largest importer of night vision gear in the US. About 8 Very Low Priced Russian (or at least Eastern bloc) different models of NVD's.

*EXPEDITION 400*

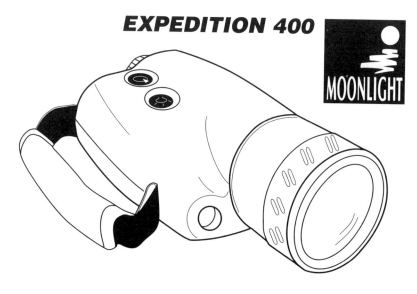

**Jensen Tools**, 7815 S. 46 St., Phoenix, AZ 85044 www.jensentools.com. Jensen sells everything else one needs to perform a successful counter measures survey, or, for that matter, do a successful bug/tap install.

Great tool kits, phone test sets, crimp down tools, wiring, color codes, cable testers, hell you can at least look like a phone repairman...

## PHD Telecommunicator

➡ **Four tools in one butt set**

➡ **Hands-free monitoring**

An enhanced test set integrating all the features of a butt set, hands-free monitor, dB signal level meter, and a digital multimeter. The LCD shows tone and pulse digits including on/off time and dB level for tones, or percentage of break, pulses per second and interdigit time. Monitors the line status (on or off-hook), zero volt intervals and non DTMF voice band tones. DMM measures AC and DC volts to 199.9 and DC current to 199.9mA. (USA)

### MICROTEST®

### Fiber Solution Kit

Tests and qualifies fiber optic LAN links. Confirms bad fiber cables. FiberLight outputs a stable, known amount of light. FiberEye detects amount of light received at the far end, then reports attenuation. Kit includes FiberEye, FiberLight, 3' cable with ST connectors, canvas case and four AA batteries. One year warranty. (USA)

**Contact East Inc.**, 335 Willow St., North Andover, MA 01845 www.conctacteast.com. Same day shipping on tools and test units.

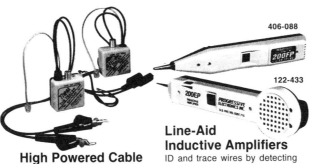

### High Powered Cable Tone Generators

• Use with inductive amplifiers
• Tones up to 50,000 ft. away
• Tones thru telco DC voltages

Tone generator with +7dB output, also features a LED indicator for polarity, AC voltage & continuity. Choose between PN 122-900 with standard alligator clips and PN 406-089 with deluxe, angled telco clips for working in restricted areas. Both units have a RJ11 plug cord, use a 9V battery (not incl.) and are 2.5" x 2.25" x 1.25".

### Line-Aid Inductive Amplifiers

ID and trace wires by detecting tones from a tone generator without penetrating or damaging wire insulation. The basic Model 200B features a weather-resistant Mylar speaker. Model 200EP is enhanced with recessed ears for butt-in testers and adjustable volume control for precise tracing of individual wires. Model 200FP adds the ability to filter out power-related noise that can drown out cable tracing tones. All units use a 9V alkaline battery (not included).

### Tone / Probe Kits

Get added convenience plus save money by choosing one of these three popular toner and probe kits. The Basic Kit includes Part Nos. 122-900 & 122-431. The Enhanced Kit includes Part Nos. 122-900 & 122-433. The Premier Kit includes Part Nos. 406-089 & 406-088. All kits include a tough nylon, belt-loop case.

**Criminal Research Products Inc.**, POB 408 Conshohocken, PA 19428. "Birthplace of the fingerprint industry." CRP makes every conceivable type of fingerprint finder and also carries some great binoculars, flashlights and forensic lights.

## Regular Fingerprint Folding Kit

**PRODUCT NO. 49-382** This regular model fingerprint taking kit contains all the necessary materials for recording fingerprints. Specially constructed of leatherette covered hardwood. The entire unit folds in half for storage and opens up for fingerprint taking convenience. An excellent addition to any department with fingerprint taking responsibilities.

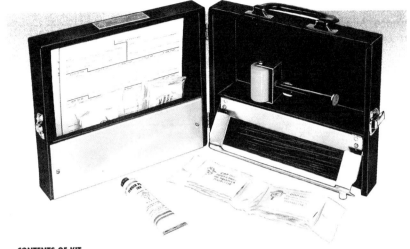

**CONTENTS OF KIT:**

1- Professional Leatherette Covered Carrying Case
    Dimensions: 10¹/₂" x 9" x 2¹/₂"
1- Fingerprint Inking Slab, mounted
1- Fingerprint Cardholder, mounted

1- 2 oz. Tube Fingerprint Ink
1- 2" Fingerprint Ink Roller
10- 8"x 8" Fingerprint Cards
20- Ink Remover Towelettes

**Northrop Grumman** 114 Union Valley Rd., Oak Ridge, TN 37830. Things just like you used to dream of when Santa brought you that first Lego kit.

But these work and go places and do things you don't want to...

**Otto Communications** 2 East Main St., Carpentersville, IL 60110 www.ottoeng.com. Low profile earphones and microphones. Not as covert as the in-ear induction or receivers, these units employ a clear acoustic tube for audio dispersion.

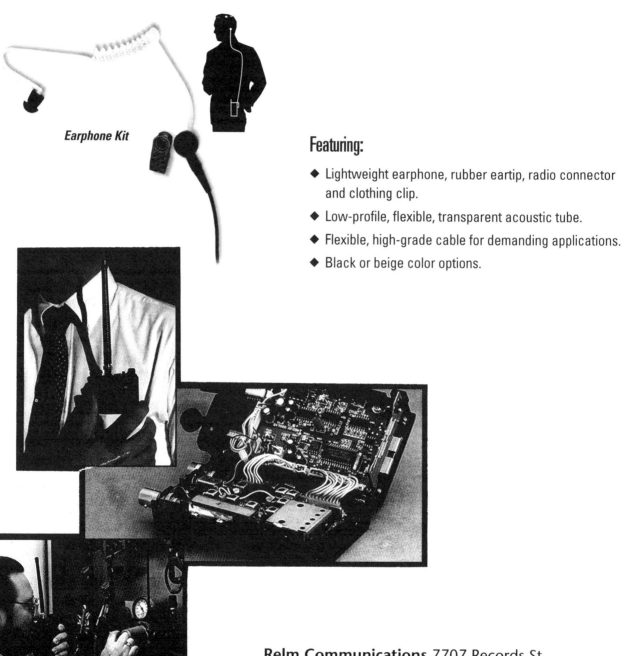

*Earphone Kit*

## Featuring:

◆ Lightweight earphone, rubber eartip, radio connector and clothing clip.

◆ Low-profile, flexible, transparent acoustic tube.

◆ Flexible, high-grade cable for demanding applications.

◆ Black or beige color options.

**Relm Communications** 7707 Records St., Indianapolis, IN 46226. Scanning transceivers. Listen to what's out there, lock into a channel and, wow, you can be talking to your favorite cop, fed, security guard or other mobile user...

Great for adapting to existing systems, using repeaters and so on.

**Hobby Lobby** 5614 Franklin Pike Circle, Brentwood, TN 37027 www.hobby-lobby.com. Low and slow electric sail planes, remote controlled mini-cars, the occasional submarine or two – all of which could accept a mini video camera and transmitter…

### Only 2 hours from box open to high performance thermal SOARING!

**GR4505 Graupner "Bussard" ARF Electric Glider .... $249.00**
Capable of soaring for hours! Pre-built and covered 2-piece geodetic handmade balsa and spruce wing will not twist. Tail parts are ready-built and covered. Entire airplane can be transported in the carrying case it comes in. Uses the "Perfekt-Fertigrumpf" UHU fuselage that's so ready-to-use that it even has pushrod cutouts, air intakes, switch cutouts done. Even the canopy is painted. Bussard can literally be flying, maybe even winning a contest, 2 hours after you get it! Wingspan: 78" (2 meter), Length: 39", Wing Area: 584 sq. in., Wing loading ca: 14 oz./sq.ft., Airfoil: SPICA mod. High performance airfoil for maximum thermal soaring duration., Weight: 56 oz.

*Here's EVERYTHING you'll need to assemble and FLY "Bussard":*

**MWK Industries** 1269 W. Pomona, CA 91720 www.mwkindurstries.com. Lasers from diode pointers to 50 watt medical units that will burn a hole in your neighbor's helicopter.

Plus, IR tubes, pinhole lenses, optical stuff.

## New 1,300nm LASER-Diode Amplifier/Transcievers

These units were probably designed for long-distance fiber-optic communication applications. They have an optical output of -8db at 1,300nm, and have two fiber-optic cables, one for signal input and another for an amplified signal output. Both cables are terminated with connectors. These units were NEVER USED, and are expensive when purchased from the manufacturer. Each unit comes with it's own test-spec' sheet. Brand New in original manufacturer's packaging.

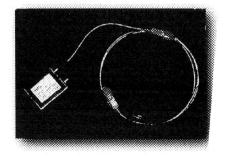

*ITEM 1300TRCNX* Our Price - $50.00

**AVO International** 4651 S. Westmoreland Road, Dallas, TX 75237 www.avointl.com. Exclusive dealers for Biddle, a firm which makes some of the more useful and lower priced TDR's around.

A TDR is one of the most essential pieces of counter surveillance gear available and just about the only thing that will actually track down faults, and taps on a telephone line.

**iis** 910 15th Street, 7th Floor, Denver, CO 80202 www.lisnet.com. Pioneers of the 800 # ID technique for finding people. One rents an 800 toll free phone number from iis which includes a voice mail trap and/or real time call out service and then places calls to anyone who might know your "friend's" location leaving an appropriate message that will inspire him to call you back.

The service immediately provides the called-from phone number.

The second alternative is to purchase a prepaid phone calling card and pass it along to the subject via some creative method ("congratulations you are a winner"). All calls made from the slick looking phone card will automatically forward both the number called from and called to, to your attention...

## You're one in a million!

Global Communications is launching an incredible new calling card. And, because the best way to get people excited about something new is to let them try it for themselves, we're conducting a **free trial offer** to people all across the country. We're giving you the opportunity to try our service by using the attached card to make **$50 worth of free local or long distance calls from any phone to anywhere in the world!** There's absolutely no charge. No hassle. And no obligation to renew the card when the free trial period expires.

## We're betting you'll like it.

How can we make such an incredible offer? Simple. We believe our customers will be our best salespeople. And when the word gets out about our exciting new calling card, we're betting everyone will want one of their own.

**It's easy.** You can use our card at any time to call anyone from any phone — from pay phones, home, hotels, airports, work, school or on the street.

**It's free.** But only for you, and only for a limited time. So go ahead, make some calls, and see for yourself how easy this new way of calling is When you've made your $50 of free calls, and you'd like to keep on saving, just call us at **1-800-897-8824**, Monday- Friday, 8:00 - 5:00 (MST).